SUPER EASY RENAL DIET COOKBOOK FOR BEGINNERS

1700 Days of Quick & Healthy Recipes to Manage Kidney Health - Low Sodium, Low Potassium, and Low Phosphorus Meals with Easy 30-Day Meal Plan

Baylei Lambert

Table of contens

Chapter 1: Understanding the Basics of the Renal Diet

Embarking on the journey to understand and manage kidney health is both essential and enlightening. The kidneys, two vital bean-shaped organs located on either side of the spine below the rib cage, play a critical role in the human body. They are responsible for filtering blood, removing waste through urine, maintaining electrolyte balance, regulating blood pressure, and ensuring the production of red blood cells. These functions are fundamental to the smooth and efficient operation of the body, underscoring the importance of the kidneys in overall health and well-being.

Dietary habits play a crucial role in maintaining kidney health and preventing or managing kidney disease. The foods and beverages we consume can either support kidney function or place additional strain on these organs, potentially worsening conditions for individuals with kidney health issues. This foundational knowledge paves the way for exploring the renal diet, a therapeutic strategy aimed at supporting kidney function and reducing the burden on these essential organs.

The Importance of the Renal Diet: Kidney Functions and How Nutrition Affects Their Health

Beyond simple filtration, the kidneys participate in a complex network of functions critical for maintaining the body's homeostasis. They filter approximately 120 to 150 quarts of blood daily, producing 1 to 2 quarts of urine that contains waste and extra fluid. Additionally, the kidneys regulate the body's salt, potassium, and acid content, which in turn aids in blood pressure control. They also produce hormones that influence other organs' functions, such as erythropoietin for red blood cell production and renin for blood pressure regulation.

Diet has a dual role in kidney health. A balanced diet supports efficient kidney function and overall well-being, while a diet high in specific nutrients like sodium, potassium, and phosphorus can increase the kidneys' workload, potentially exacerbating health issues for those with kidney disease. For those with compromised kidney function, it is crucial to manage the dietary intake of these nutrients to prevent the accumulation of substances the kidneys cannot filter effectively.

Protein consumption, for instance, requires careful management in renal diets to prevent unnecessary strain on the kidneys. Similarly, excessive sodium intake can lead to increased blood pressure, swelling, and fluid retention, complicating kidney health. The management of potassium and phosphorus is also vital to prevent their levels from becoming harmful due to the kidneys' reduced excretion capacity.

The renal diet aims to mitigate the adverse effects of certain nutrients on kidney function while ensuring the body receives the necessary nutrition. Its primary goals include:

- Limiting sodium intake to manage blood pressure and prevent fluid retention.

- Controlling protein consumption to reduce the kidneys' workload.

- Regulating potassium and phosphorus levels to avoid dangerous blood buildups.

This diet promotes the consumption of kidney-friendly foods that meet the body's nutritional needs without overburdening the kidneys, requiring careful planning and knowledge of beneficial foods and those to limit or avoid.

Mastering Micronutrients: Managing Sodium, Potassium, and Phosphorus

Sodium in the Renal Diet

Sodium, an essential electrolyte, is crucial for maintaining fluid balance, aiding nerve transmission, and supporting muscle contractions. However, excessive sodium can lead to increased blood pressure, putting additional strain on the kidneys. High sodium intake can cause water retention, increasing blood volume and pressure, which can damage blood vessels leading to the kidneys and exacerbate kidney disease. Adopting a low-sodium diet entails careful food selection and preparation, including reading labels to avoid high-sodium products and opting for fresh over processed foods.

Potassium Management

Potassium is vital for heart and muscle function, regulating heartbeat and muscle contractions. Kidney disease can impair the body's ability to balance potassium levels, making its management essential in the renal diet. Elevated potassium levels can cause dangerous heart rhythms and even cardiac arrest. Managing potassium intake involves choosing low-potassium foods and being mindful of portion sizes and preparation methods.

Phosphorus Control

Phosphorus is key to building strong bones and teeth, muscle recovery, and nerve signaling. However, managing phosphorus is challenging for those with kidney disease, as impaired kidneys may not effectively remove excess phosphorus. High phosphorus levels can weaken bones and contribute to cardiovascular disease. Managing phosphorus intake involves consuming fresh, whole foods and limiting foods with added phosphates.

FAQs and Common Myths about the Renal Diet Unveiled

Embarking on the renal diet journey can evoke a mix of emotions and questions. It's essential to separate fact from fiction to navigate effectively. This section addresses common inquiries, debunks myths, and offers practical advice for integrating the renal diet into daily life.

FAQs:

Eating Out: It's possible to enjoy dining out with adjustments, such as choosing restaurants that offer fresh, customizable dishes and requesting modifications like no added salt.

Protein Intake: Protein management on the renal diet involves consuming enough high-quality protein to maintain health without overburdening the kidneys. Lean meats, poultry, fish, and plant-based proteins are part of a balanced diet, with intake tailored to individual needs.

Dietary Restrictions: Focus on what you can eat, explore new kidney-friendly foods, and use herbs and spices for flavor to make the renal diet manageable and enjoyable.

Myths vs. Facts:

- **High Protein Myth:** The renal diet emphasizes moderate, not high, protein intake, tailored to individual needs.

- **Fruits and Vegetables Myth:** Fruits and vegetables are essential, with some needing limitation based on potassium or phosphorus content.

- **Dairy Products Myth:** Not all dairy products are off-limits; some low-phosphorus options can be included in moderation.

Implementing the renal diet involves meal planning, cooking tips to enhance flavors without harmful additives, and modifying recipes to fit dietary needs.

Conclusion

Understanding kidney health and the dietary impact is crucial. The renal diet is more than a set of restrictions; it's a comprehensive eating approach that prioritizes kidney health while allowing for varied and enjoyable meals. By managing micronutrients and adopting innovative cooking techniques, we can protect kidney function and improve overall well-being. This chapter aims to empower you with the knowledge to make informed dietary choices for kidney health.

Next Steps

- **Educate Yourself Further:** Continue seeking information on kidney health and the renal diet.

- **Consult Healthcare Professionals:** Regularly check in with healthcare providers and dietitians specialized in renal health for personalized advice.

- **Experiment in the Kitchen:** Get creative with meals, exploring new recipes and safe substitutions.

- **Join Support Groups:** Connect with others navigating the renal diet for encouragement and practical tips.

- **Monitor Your Health:** Keep a close eye on kidney function and overall health with regular tests and check-ups.

- **Advocate for Your Health:** Communicate dietary needs when dining out or at social gatherings.

- **Reflect and Adjust:** Managing a renal diet is an ongoing process; be open to adjustments based on health, preferences, and lifestyle changes.

Embarking on the renal diet journey is a significant step towards controlling your kidney health. With the right tools, information, and mindset, this path can lead to a healthier, more vibrant life. Let this chapter serve as the foundation for your journey towards optimal kidney health and overall wellness.

Chapter 2: Preparing for the Renal Diet

Embarking on a renal diet journey requires a profound understanding of how nutrition affects kidney health. This chapter, dedicated to Nutritional Planning Strategies, aims to empower individuals with the knowledge and tools to craft meals that are not only nourishing and fulfilling but also kidney-friendly. By focusing on understanding nutritional needs, mastering meal planning basics, and learning how to balance the plate, readers will be equipped to make informed dietary choices that support their kidney health.

Understanding the body's nutritional needs is crucial in managing any health condition, including kidney disease. The kidneys play a vital role in filtering waste from the blood, balancing electrolytes, and regulating blood pressure. When kidney function is compromised, it becomes essential to monitor certain nutrients closely to prevent further strain on these organs.

Key Nutrients to Monitor:

- **Sodium:** High sodium intake can increase blood pressure, potentially leading to kidney damage. Limiting sodium intake can help manage blood pressure and reduce kidney strain.

- **Potassium:** Essential for nerve and muscle function, but excessive potassium can be harmful when kidneys cannot effectively filter it, possibly leading to heart problems.

- **Phosphorus:** Elevated phosphorus levels can cause bone and cardiovascular issues in those with kidney disease, as damaged kidneys can't remove excess phosphorus.

- **Protein:** Protein is crucial for bodily functions, but in kidney disease, the amount and type of protein consumed need careful management to prevent waste buildup.

Understanding these nutritional needs is the first step toward planning a kidney-friendly diet, which involves knowing which foods to limit and identifying those that can help maintain optimal health.

Meal Planning Basics

Meal planning is a powerful tool, especially for individuals managing kidney health. It ensures that meals throughout the week align with renal diet guidelines, satisfying hunger and taste preferences while keeping nutrient intake in check.

Steps to Effective Meal Planning:

1. **Educate Yourself:** Learn about foods high in sodium, potassium, and phosphorus, and find healthier alternatives.

2. **Consult with a Dietitian:** A healthcare professional specializing in renal diets can offer personalized advice based on your kidney health needs.

3. **Plan Your Meals:** Draft a week's menu, including all meals and snacks. This aids in diet management and streamlines grocery shopping.

4. **Prepare in Advance:** Preparing meals ahead of time can help you stay on track, particularly on busy days when cooking might be challenging.

Incorporating a variety of foods within the renal diet's guidelines can prevent mealtime monotony. Experimenting with different herbs and spices can also enhance flavor without relying on salt or other restricted ingredients.

Creating balanced meals is essential in a renal diet. It's about more than just limiting certain nutrients; it's ensuring that each meal provides the necessary vitamins, minerals, and energy for overall health without overburdening the kidneys.

*   **Fill Half Your Plate with Vegetables and Fruits:** Opt for those lower in potassium to manage intake, such as apples, berries, carrots, and green beans.

*   **Include Lean Proteins:** Select high-quality protein sources lower in phosphorus and prepare them healthily. Fish, egg whites, and poultry are excellent options.

*   **Select Whole Grains:** Whole grains offer energy and fiber. However, some grains are high in phosphorus, necessitating portion control.

*   **Limit High-Sodium Condiments:** Dressings, sauces, and dips can be high in sodium. Prefer homemade alternatives where ingredient control is possible.

By adhering to these guidelines, individuals can enjoy varied and flavorful meals that support kidney health. The objective is not merely to restrict certain foods but to discover a balance that fosters overall well-being.

Smart Grocery Shopping Guide for the Renal Diet

Embarking on a renal diet necessitates a thoughtful approach to grocery shopping. This guide is crafted to navigate you through the aisles of your local supermarket with a discerning eye for renal-friendly foods, ensuring that your shopping cart aligns with your dietary needs. Delving into label reading, essential shopping lists, and avoiding common pitfalls, this chapter aims to make your grocery shopping experience both stress-free and conducive to kidney health.

Understanding Nutritional Labels

When managing kidney health, paying close attention to sodium, potassium, and phosphorus in food products is crucial, as these nutrients directly impact the effectiveness of your renal diet. Mastery in reading and interpreting food labels is essential. Focus on the "Nutrition Facts" panel found on packaging, scrutinizing the milligrams of sodium, potassium, and phosphorus per serving. Monitoring protein levels is also vital, particularly if your dietary needs require adjustment based on the stage of your kidney disease.

Be mindful of serving sizes, as they can be misleading. A package might appear suitable for a single meal, yet the label may indicate it contains multiple servings, necessitating an adjustment in nutrient totals if consuming more than one serving. This aspect is especially significant for sodium and potassium, where exceeding the recommended serving size can inadvertently surpass your daily nutrient limits.

Crafting a Renal-Friendly Shopping List

A meticulously prepared shopping list serves as your primary defense against the challenges and temptations of grocery shopping. Start with fresh fruits and vegetables that are low in potassium, like apples, berries, carrots, and cauliflower. Include lean proteins such as chicken, turkey, and fish, complemented by whole grains lower in phosphorus like rice, barley, and bulgur wheat. Don't overlook the importance of healthy fats, such as olive oil, and calcium-rich foods with low phosphorus content, including certain hard cheeses and non-dairy milk alternatives.

Your shopping list should encompass various categories to ensure a well-rounded diet:

- **Vegetables and Fruits:** Prioritize low-potassium selections.

- **Proteins:** Opt for lean meats, poultry, fish, and plant-based proteins.

- **Dairy and Alternatives:** Choose low-phosphorus milk alternatives.

- **Grains:** Select whole grains that are lower in phosphorus.

- **Snacks:** Seek out options low in sodium and phosphorus.

Navigating the Grocery Store

Awareness of which foods to avoid is as important as knowing what to include. High-sodium offenders typically include processed meats, canned soups, and salty snacks. For potassium, be wary of bananas, potatoes, and oranges. Phosphorus-laden pitfalls often involve processed foods and certain dairy products, notorious for added phosphates.

Adhering to your renal diet amidst the vast selection available in grocery stores can pose a challenge. Here are strategies to keep you aligned with your dietary goals:

- **Shop with a List:** Commit to shopping with a list to prevent diverging into impulse buys that don't meet your renal diet criteria.

- **Eat Before You Shop:** Avoid shopping hungry to curb the inclination towards impulsive, potentially non-compliant purchases.

- **Know the Store Layout:** Familiarize yourself with the location of renal-friendly foods to steer clear of aisles that tempt with restricted items.

- **Consider Online Grocery Shopping:** Where possible, online shopping can diminish impulse buying, enabling direct searches for list-specific items.

This comprehensive approach to grocery shopping is designed to support individuals on a renal diet, facilitating informed choices that promote kidney health while enjoying a diverse and nutritious diet.

Adapting Your Kitchen for the Renal Diet: Essentials for a Kidney-Friendly Kitchen

Embarking on a renal diet journey necessitates not just an adjustment in your diet but also how you prepare your meals. Creating a kidney-friendly kitchen is fundamental to this new dietary path, ensuring a smooth transition to healthier cooking habits. This chapter focuses on transforming your kitchen into a supportive environment for your renal diet, aiming to make meal preparation both enjoyable and conducive to your health goals.

A well-organized kitchen is pivotal to renal-friendly cooking. Start by decluttering your pantry and refrigerator, eliminating items incompatible with your dietary requirements. This action not only creates space but also reduces temptation. Organize your food storage by categories, such as low-sodium spices, low-potassium fruits and vegetables, and phosphorus-friendly dairy alternatives. Clearly labeling these categories can expedite the process of identifying the correct ingredients for your meals.

Stocking Your Pantry

A pantry conducive to a renal diet contains essentials that accommodate dietary restrictions without stifling culinary creativity:

- **Whole Grains:** Opt for bulgur wheat, buckwheat, and couscous as nutritious staples.

- **Low-Sodium Broths:** Stock up on a variety of beans, lentils, and low-sodium broths to enrich flavors.

- **Herbs and Spices:** Maintain a diverse array of herbs and spices for seasoning without the need for salt.

- **Canned Goods:** Choose low-sodium or no-salt-added options, rinsing them thoroughly before use to further reduce sodium content.

Essential Kitchen Gadgets

Certain tools can significantly ease the preparation of kidney-friendly meals:

- **Chef's Knife and Cutting Boards:** Essential for efficiently chopping fresh produce.

- **Slow Cooker/Pressure Cooker:** Ideal for preparing grains, legumes, and making low-sodium stews and soups.

- **Measuring Tools:** Cups and spoons are vital for accurately controlling portion sizes and nutrient intake.

- **Spice Grinder/Mortar and Pestle:** Useful for creating your own salt-free seasoning blends.

- **High-Powered Blender:** Perfect for making smoothies and soups from low-potassium fruits and vegetables.

- **Vegetable Steamer:** Aids in nutrient preservation while minimizing the need for added fats or salts.

Adapting Recipes

Adapting recipes to fit a renal diet often requires substituting high-sodium, potassium, and phosphorus ingredients with healthier alternatives:

- **Salt Substitutes:** Use a mix of dried herbs, spices, vinegar, or lemon juice for flavor enhancement without adding sodium.

- **Milk Alternatives:** Choose rice or almond milk as lower-phosphorus substitutes for dairy milk.

- **Potassium Reduction:** Opt for low-potassium fruits and vegetables like apples, berries, carrots, and green beans as substitutes for higher-potassium options.

Embracing these substitutions not only maintains the kidney-friendliness of your meals but also opens up a new world of flavors and textures. Experiment with nutritional yeast for a phosphorus-friendly cheesy flavor or roasted red pepper sauce as a high-potassium tomato sauce alternative. Creativity in your substitutions ensures your meals remain aligned with your renal diet while introducing exciting new culinary experiences.

Culinary Creativity on a Renal Diet

Adapting to a renal diet necessitates a significant shift in our approach to cooking and flavor. This journey emphasizes the reduction of sodium, potassium, and phosphorus intake to safeguard kidney health, all while preserving the pleasure of consuming flavorful meals. This chapter delves into innovative cooking techniques and tips that enhance flavor while adhering to the guidelines of a renal diet, ensuring that meals remain both safe and satisfyingly rich in taste.

1. Seasoning without Salt

The task of lowering sodium intake might appear challenging at first, given salt's role as a primary flavor enhancer across numerous cuisines. Yet, the world of culinary arts abounds with herbs, spices, and other natural flavor enhancers that can elevate a dish without necessitating the use of salt.

- **Herbs and Spices:** Incorporating fresh herbs like parsley, cilantro, dill, and basil can infuse dishes with vibrant flavors, bypassing the need for sodium. Dry spices such as cumin, paprika, turmeric, and black pepper bring depth and complexity to meals. Experimenting with various herb and spice combinations can yield delicious flavor profiles.

- **Acidic Ingredients:** A dash of lemon juice or vinegar can enhance a dish, providing a tangy zest that compensates for the absence of salt, slicing through the richness and elevating the overall flavor.

- **Aromatics:** Ingredients like garlic, onions, shallots, and ginger lay a flavorful foundation for dishes without introducing harmful nutrients, offering robust flavors that enrich the culinary experience.

2. Cooking Methods

The techniques employed in cooking not only influence flavor but also affect nutrient retention and the healthfulness of meals. Selecting cooking methods that preserve the nutritional integrity of ingredients while limiting unwanted nutrients is essential.

- **Steaming and Poaching:** These gentle methods maintain the natural flavors and nutrients of foods without the addition of excess fats or salts, preserving the food's inherent qualities.

- **Roasting and Grilling:** By caramelizing and charring, these techniques reveal the natural sweetness and complexity of foods, adding depth to vegetables and lean proteins without resorting to unhealthy additives.

- **Slow Cooking:** Utilizing slow cookers fosters the blending of flavors over extended periods, allowing for the creation of richly flavored dishes effortlessly and without the need for additional sodium or harmful ingredients.

3. Recipe Reimagining

Converting traditional recipes to fit within the constraints of a renal diet involves both creativity and adaptability. The aim is to preserve the essence of a dish while ensuring it remains kidney-friendly.

- **Ingredient Swaps:** Substituting high-sodium, potassium, and phosphorus ingredients with alternatives that mimic their textures and flavors is key. For example, opting for rice milk or almond milk as lower-phosphorus alternatives to dairy milk or using cauliflower in place of potatoes as a low-potassium substitute.

- **Rethinking Techniques:** Modifying cooking techniques to avoid renal diet non-compliant ingredients can significantly impact a dish's suitability. For instance, roasting vegetables instead of boiling them can concentrate flavors and retain more nutrients.

- **Portion Adjustment:** At times, simply adjusting the portion sizes of dishes can help manage nutrient levels, making it possible to enjoy a wider variety of foods within the diet's guidelines.

Through embracing these strategies, individuals on a renal diet can enjoy a rich tapestry of flavors and textures, transforming dietary limitations into opportunities for culinary exploration and enjoyment.

Recipe Modifications for Health

Embracing the renal diet transcends mere avoidance of certain foods; it's about reenvisioning your plate and uncovering new ways to relish your favorite meals. This chapter ventures into the essence of modifying recipes for health, spotlighting creative substitutions and the pivotal role of portion control in maintaining a kidney-friendly diet.

Creative Substitutions

At the heart of recipe modification is the craft of identifying innovative alternatives for ingredients that don't align with kidney health, without sacrificing flavor or satisfaction. These creative substitutions help ensure meals stay delicious and adhere to the guidelines of a renal diet.

- **Rethinking Proteins:** Opt for leaner protein options to replace high-phosphorus meats. Skinless chicken or turkey can substitute for red meats, while plant-based proteins such as lentils and chickpeas offer lower potassium alternatives to some animal proteins.

- **Low-Potassium Vegetables:** Substitute high-potassium vegetables like potatoes with cauliflower, which can be mashed or roasted to create a tasty side dish, providing versatility and flavor without the potassium load.

- **Herbs and Spices Over Salt:** A blend of fresh herbs (basil, cilantro, dill) and dry spices (turmeric, paprika, garlic powder) can enrich dishes with robust flavors, circumventing the need for salt and high-sodium seasonings.

- **Grain Choices:** Select bases for dishes from grains such as rice, bulgur, or couscous, which are lower in phosphorus than quinoa or some whole grains. Mindful portion control is crucial even with these lower-phosphorus alternatives.

Portion Control

Grasping and applying portion control is essential in managing the intake of nutrients critical to kidney health, such as sodium, potassium, and phosphorus. It enables the enjoyment of a diverse array of foods while monitoring nutrient consumption.

- **Visual Guides:** Employ visual cues to determine appropriate portion sizes—a meat serving should equate to the size of a deck of cards, while a grain serving might fit in the palm of your hand.

- **Measuring Tools:** Consistent use of measuring cups, spoons, and food scales aids in accurately measuring serving sizes, facilitating adherence to dietary guidelines.

- **Plate Method:** Strategically divide your plate to balance nutrient intake: half filled with low-potassium vegetables, one quarter with lean protein, and the remaining quarter with grains or starches.

Through these strategies, individuals on a renal diet can navigate the complexities of dietary restrictions with ease, transforming limitations into opportunities for culinary exploration and enjoyment. This approach not only safeguards kidney health but also enriches the dining experience with a spectrum of flavors and textures.

Dining Out: Navigating Restaurants on a Renal Diet

While a renal diet typically emphasizes home-cooked meals, dining out remains an enjoyable part of social life that doesn't have to be entirely eliminated. This chapter offers guidance for those following a renal diet on how to enjoy restaurant dining without compromising kidney health, covering strategies for choosing suitable restaurants, effectively communicating dietary restrictions, and selecting safe menu options that comply with renal dietary guidelines.

Choosing the Right Restaurants

Successful dining out starts with selecting establishments likely to accommodate dietary needs. Restaurants offering fresh, made-to-order dishes are generally more adaptable to modifications than those reliant on pre-prepared foods. Utilizing online menus and reviews can aid in evaluating a restaurant's flexibility and menu variety. Many now provide nutritional information online, facilitating informed choices. Ethnic cuisines such as Mediterranean or Japanese often naturally fit renal diet restrictions, offering grilled meats, fresh salads, and renal-friendly fish dishes.

Communicating Dietary Restrictions

Effective communication is key when dining out. Inform your server of your dietary restrictions, emphasizing their health importance, and be specific about your needs (e.g., "I need to avoid high-sodium options"). Suggesting simple modifications, like sauces on the side or no added salt, can make it easier for the kitchen to accommodate. For those with extensive dietary restrictions, a "chef card" listing these can be invaluable in clearly communicating your needs directly to kitchen staff.

Safe Menu Options

Opt for dishes prepared through steaming, grilling, or baking, as these methods typically minimize oil and salt use. Avoid fried and breaded items, usually high in sodium and phosphorus. Lean proteins, steamed or grilled vegetables within low-potassium guidelines, and salads or customizable dishes with dressing on the side are safer choices, allowing for control over ingredients to adhere to your renal diet.

Conclusion

Adapting to a renal diet might seem challenging initially, but with appropriate strategies and creativity, enjoying a varied, flavorful, and healthful diet that supports kidney health is entirely achievable. This chapter provides the tools and knowledge to confidently tackle the renal diet's challenges, making it a sustainable and enriching part of your lifestyle. Whether preparing meals at home or dining out, the provided tips will ensure you can maintain a kidney-friendly diet without missing out on the joy of eating.

Next Steps

As you grow more accustomed to these foundational strategies, you're poised to delve deeper into the world of renal-friendly recipes and cuisines. The path to kidney health via diet is an ongoing journey of learning, offering ample opportunities for culinary exploration and satisfaction with every meal.

Chapter 3: Living a Kidney-Friendly Lifestyle

Sticking to the Special Diet

Embarking on the journey of a renal diet is a critical move towards protecting kidney health and improving overall well-being. This section provides essential knowledge and strategies for confidently and consistently following this path.

Dietary Discipline

The renal diet is carefully structured to minimize kidney strain by restricting nutrients like sodium, potassium, and phosphorus. Key to this diet is knowing which foods to favor and which to avoid. Antioxidant-rich and mineral-low foods such as cauliflower, blueberries, and bell peppers are beneficial, whereas processed foods and certain dairy products may be harmful due to their high sodium and phosphorus levels.

Adherence begins with careful meal planning and preparation, incorporating a diverse array of kidney-friendly foods to ensure nutritional balance and avoid monotony. Seeking recipes that comply with dietary restrictions, either through online resources or consultation with a dietitian, is advisable. Meal prep in advance can ease the burden of daily cooking, suggesting a day dedicated to batch cooking with meals stored in clearly labeled containers for the week ahead.

Navigating holidays and social events, often centered around food, poses a significant challenge. Preparing by bringing a diet-compliant dish to share ensures a safe dining option is available. Open communication about dietary needs with hosts can lead to accommodations, focusing on the event's joy rather than dietary limitations, emphasizing moderation.

Eating out, while seemingly daunting on a renal diet, is manageable with research and preparation. Reviewing the menu ahead of time, asking servers about dish preparation, and requesting modifications can make dining out enjoyable and safe. Opting for steamed, grilled, or baked dishes over fried ones, and monitoring portion sizes, helps maintain control over nutrient intake.

Maintaining a renal diet demands commitment, foresight, and a proactive stance towards potential challenges. By understanding kidney-supportive dietary needs, engaging in thoughtful meal planning, and navigating social and dining-out situations with strategy, individuals can successfully manage their renal diet and embrace a kidney-friendly lifestyle.

Maintaining a Healthy Weight

A healthy weight is vital in managing kidney health, especially for those on a renal diet. This section explores the relationship between body weight and kidney function, offering guidance on achieving a weight that fosters both kidney health and overall wellness.

Excess weight directly impacts kidney health by overburdening the organs, increasing the risk of hypertension and type 2 diabetes, leading causes of kidney disease. Obesity can also lead to "obesity-related glomerulopathy," damaging the kidneys over time due to increased workload and metabolic demands.

Maintaining a healthy weight involves a balanced approach to eating and regular physical activity. Here are strategies to support weight management:

- **Prioritize Nutrient-Dense Foods:** Incorporate a variety of fruits, vegetables, lean proteins, and whole grains into your diet, mindful of potassium and phosphorus levels.

- **Control Portions:** Utilize measuring tools and visual cues to manage portion sizes effectively, aiding in caloric intake management without strict calorie counting.

- **Plan Meals:** Meal planning helps avoid impulsive eating decisions, ensuring choices support both renal health and weight management.

Regular physical activity is essential for weight maintenance, enhancing cardiovascular health, muscle tone, and overall well-being.

- **Find Enjoyable Activities:** Choose physical activities that you enjoy to encourage regular participation.

- **Set Realistic Goals:** Begin with manageable exercises, gradually increasing intensity and duration to build consistency and long-term success.

- **Seek Professional Guidance:** Consult healthcare professionals before starting a new exercise regimen to tailor activities to your health needs.

Achieving and maintaining a healthy weight is crucial for kidney health management. Through balanced nutrition and consistent physical activity, individuals can cultivate a lifestyle that not only supports their renal diet but also promotes broader health and well-being, empowering them with the strategies necessary for a fulfilling and healthy life.

Managing Blood Sugar and Blood Pressure Levels

For optimal kidney health, managing blood sugar and blood pressure levels is essential. This section explores their impact on kidney function and provides guidance on controlling diabetes or prediabetes and hypertension through mindful dietary and lifestyle adjustments.

Blood Sugar Control

Chronic high blood sugar can significantly harm the kidneys, leading to diabetic nephropathy. A diet rich in whole, nutrient-dense foods is crucial for managing blood sugar levels. Incorporating non-starchy vegetables, lean proteins, whole grains, and healthy fats can stabilize blood sugar. Regular physical activity and stress management techniques also play vital roles in maintaining blood sugar levels.

Blood Pressure Management

High blood pressure can severely affect kidney function. The DASH diet is recommended for managing blood pressure, emphasizing fruits, vegetables, whole grains, and lean proteins. Limiting sodium intake and engaging in regular physical activity are also key. Stress reduction techniques can further aid in managing blood pressure.

Managing blood sugar and blood pressure through dietary choices and lifestyle changes is crucial for kidney health.

Limiting Alcohol Intake and Quitting Smoking

A holistic approach to a kidney-friendly lifestyle includes moderating alcohol intake and quitting smoking, alongside regular health screenings.

Moderation with Alcohol

Excessive alcohol consumption can adversely affect kidney function. Guidelines suggest limiting intake to one drink per day for women and two for men. For those with advanced kidney disease, abstaining from alcohol may be advisable.

Quitting Smoking for Kidney Health

Smoking directly harms the kidneys and increases the risk of kidney cancer. Quitting smoking is crucial, with strategies including setting a quit date, identifying triggers, and utilizing support resources like quitlines and smoking cessation programs.

Regular Health Screenings for Optimal Kidney Care

Regular screenings are vital for early detection of kidney damage. These include serum creatinine tests, urine tests for protein, and blood pressure measurements. Effective communication with healthcare providers is essential for coordinated care and understanding of test results and treatment plans.

Adopting these practices is key to maintaining kidney health and overall well-being.

Conclusion

Adopting a kidney-friendly lifestyle involves making health-conscious decisions that support kidney function and overall well-being. This chapter offers a comprehensive guide to integrating these practices into daily life, providing a solid foundation for those dedicated to maintaining kidney health. By embracing the strategies detailed here, individuals can confidently manage their renal health, ensuring a balanced and healthy lifestyle that benefits their kidneys.

Chapter 4: Recipes for Every Meal

Morning Magic: 20 Kick-Start Breakfasts

1. Classic Egg White Scramble

Yield: 2 servings | Prep time: 5 minutes | Cook time: 10 minutes

Ingredients:

- 6 large egg whites
- 1 cup fresh spinach, roughly chopped
- 1/2 cup bell peppers (red and yellow), diced
- 1 tablespoon olive oi

Directions:

1. Heat the olive oil in a non-stick skillet over medium heat.
2. Add the diced bell peppers to the skillet and sauté for 2-3 minutes until they start to soften.
3. Add the chopped spinach to the skillet and sauté for an additional 1-2 minutes until the spinach wilts.
4. Pour the egg whites over the sautéed vegetables. Stir gently and cook until the egg whites are fully set, about 4-5 minutes.
5. Divide the scramble between two plates and serve immediately.

Nutritional Information:

Per serving: 150 calories, 18g protein, 5g carbohydrates, 7g fat, 1g fiber, 0mg cholesterol, 200mg sodium, 300mg potassium, 150mg phosphorus.

2. Morning Bliss Almond Milk Berry Smoothie

Yield: 2 servings | Prep time: 5 minutes | Cook time: 0 minutes

Ingredients:

- 1 cup fresh strawberries, hulled
- 1/2 cup fresh blueberries
- 1 1/2 cups unsweetened almond milk
- 1 cup ice cubes

Directions:

1. Place the strawberries, blueberries, almond milk, and ice cubes in a blender.
2. Blend on high speed until all the ingredients are thoroughly combined and the mixture is smooth.
3. Pour the smoothie into glasses and serve immediately for a refreshing and nutritious start to your day.

Nutritional Information:

Per serving: 100 calories, 2g protein, 15g carbohydrates, 3g fat, 4g fiber, 0mg cholesterol, 90mg sodium, 250mg potassium, 50mg phosphorus.

3. Sunrise Soothe Kidney-Friendly Pancakes

Yield: 4 servings | Prep time: 10 minutes | Cook time: 15 minutes

Ingredients:

- 1 cup rice flour
- 1 1/2 cups non-dairy milk (such as almond milk)
- 1 large egg
- 2 teaspoons baking powder (aluminum-free)
- 1 tablespoon olive oil (for the batter)
- Olive oil or cooking spray (for the griddle)

Directions:

1. In a large bowl, whisk together rice flour and baking powder.
2. In a separate bowl, beat the egg lightly and mix with non-dairy milk and 1 tablespoon of olive oil.
3. Gradually add the wet ingredients to the dry ingredients, whisking until a smooth batter forms.
4. Heat a non-stick griddle or skillet over medium heat and lightly coat with olive oil or cooking spray.
5. Ladle approximately 1/4 cup of batter onto the hot griddle for each pancake. Cook until bubbles form on the surface, then flip carefully and cook until golden brown on both sides and cooked through.
6. Serve warm with your choice of renal-diet-friendly toppings, such as a drizzle of honey or a sprinkle of cinnamon.

Nutritional Information:

Per serving: 200 calories, 5g protein, 35g carbohydrates, 5g fat, 1g fiber, 53mg cholesterol, 100mg sodium, 200mg potassium, 150mg phosphorus.

4. Low-Sodium Blueberry Muffins

Yield: 6 servings | Prep time: 10 minutes | Cook time: 20 minutes

Ingredients:

- 2 cups wheat flour
- 2 teaspoons low-sodium baking powder
- 1 cup fresh blueberries
- 1/2 cup unsweetened applesauce
- 1/2 cup non-dairy milk
- 1/4 cup honey or maple syrup
- 1 teaspoon vanilla extract
- 2 tablespoons olive oil

Directions:

1. Preheat the oven to 375°F (190°C) and line a muffin tin with paper liners or lightly grease with oil.
2. In a large bowl, whisk together the wheat flour and low-sodium baking powder.
3. In another bowl, mix the unsweetened applesauce, non-dairy milk, honey (or maple syrup), vanilla extract, and olive oil until well combined.
4. Gradually add the wet ingredients to the dry ingredients, stirring until just combined. Be careful not to overmix.
5. Gently fold in the fresh blueberries.
6. Divide the batter evenly among the muffin cups, filling each about 3/4 full.
7. Bake for 20 minutes, or until a toothpick inserted into the center of a muffin comes out clean.
8. Let the muffins cool in the pan for 5 minutes, then transfer to a wire rack to cool completely.

Nutritional Information:

Per serving: 220 calories, 4g protein, 45g carbohydrates, 5g fat, 3g fiber, 0mg cholesterol, 50mg sodium, 150mg potassium, 100mg phosphorus.

5. Dawn Delight Apple Cinnamon Oatmeal

Yield: 4 servings | Prep time: 5 minutes | Cook time: 10 minutes

Ingredients:

- 2 cups water
- 1 cup low-phosphorus oatmeal (quick-cooking oats)
- 1 large apple, diced
- 1 teaspoon cinnamon
- Optional sweeteners: honey or maple syrup (to taste)

Directions:

1. Bring water to a boil in a medium saucepan.
2. Stir in the oatmeal, reduce the heat to medium-low, and cook for 5 minutes, stirring occasionally.
3. When the oatmeal is nearly done, mix in the diced apple and cinnamon. Cook for an additional 2-3 minutes, until the apples are slightly softened and the oatmeal is fully cooked.
4. Remove from heat and let sit for a minute to thicken. Add honey or maple syrup to taste, if desired.
5. Serve warm, dividing the oatmeal equally among four bowls.

Nutritional Information:

Per serving: 150 calories, 4g protein, 27g carbohydrates, 2g fat, 4g fiber, 0mg cholesterol, 10mg sodium, 200mg potassium, 100mg phosphorus.

6. Fresh Start Avocado Toast on Low-Sodium Bread

Yield: 2 servings | Prep time: 5 minutes | Cook time: 2 minutes

Ingredients:

- 1 ripe avocado
- 1 teaspoon lemon juice
- 2 slices low-sodium whole grain bread

Directions:

1. Toast the whole grain bread slices to your preferred level of crispiness.
2. In a small bowl, mash the avocado with the lemon juice until it reaches a smooth consistency.
3. Spread the mashed avocado evenly over the toasted bread slices.
4. Serve immediately, optionally garnished with a sprinkle of black pepper or chili flakes for added flavor.

Nutritional Information:

Per serving: 230 calories, 6g protein, 27g carbohydrates, 14g fat, 10g fiber, 0mg cholesterol, 150mg sodium, 487mg potassium, 75mg phosphorus.

7. Cozy Cinnamon Rice Pudding

Yield: 4 servings | Prep time: 5 minutes |
Cook time: 25 minutes

Ingredients:

- 1 cup cooked white rice
- 2 cups unsweetened almond milk (or any non-dairy milk)
- 2 tablespoons sugar (adjust to taste)
- 1 teaspoon cinnamon
- Optional: a pinch of salt to enhance flavors

Directions:

1. In a medium saucepan, combine the cooked white rice, almond milk, and a pinch of salt (if using). Cook over medium heat, stirring occasionally.
2. Once the mixture begins to simmer, reduce the heat to low. Stir in the sugar and cinnamon.
3. Continue to cook, stirring frequently, until the mixture thickens to your desired consistency, about 20-25 minutes.
4. Remove from heat and allow to cool slightly. The pudding will thicken further as it cools.
5. Serve warm, or transfer to a container and chill in the refrigerator to serve cold. Garnish with a sprinkle of cinnamon before serving.

Nutritional Information:

Per serving: 180 calories, 3g protein, 38g carbohydrates, 2.5g fat, 1g fiber, 0mg cholesterol, 80mg sodium, 150mg potassium, 100mg phosphorus.

8. Sunrise Protein-Packed Egg White and Turkey Sausage Burrito

Yield: 2 servings | Prep time: 10 minutes |
Cook time: 10minutes

Ingredients:

- 4 large egg whites
- 2 low-sodium turkey sausages, fully cooked and diced
- 2 whole wheat tortillas

Directions:

1. Heat a non-stick skillet over medium heat. Add the egg whites and cook, stirring frequently, until they are fully set, about 3-4 minutes.
2. In the same skillet, add the diced turkey sausage and cook until heated through, approximately 2-3 minutes.
3. Warm the whole wheat tortillas in the microwave for 10-15 seconds or on a skillet for a few seconds on each side.
4. Divide the cooked egg whites and turkey sausage evenly among the tortillas. Place the mixture down the center of each tortilla.
5. Fold the bottom of the tortilla up over the filling, then fold in the sides and roll up tightly.
6. Serve the burritos immediately, or wrap them in foil to keep warm until serving.

Nutritional Information:

Per serving: 250 calories, 28g protein, 18g carbohydrates, 8g fat, 3g fiber, 0mg cholesterol, 400mg sodium, 300mg potassium, 150mg phosphorus.

9. Morning Glow Peachy Keen Smoothie

Yield: 2 servings | Prep time: 5 minutes | Cook time: 0 minutes

Ingredients:

- 1 cup sliced peaches (fresh or frozen)
- 1/2 cup Greek yogurt (low-fat, unsweetened)
- 1 tablespoon honey (optional)
- 1/2 cup ice

Directions:

1. Place the sliced peaches, Greek yogurt, honey (if using), and ice into a blender.
2. Blend on high until the mixture is smooth and creamy. If the smoothie is too thick, you can add a little water or additional ice to reach your desired consistency.
3. Pour the smoothie into glasses and serve immediately for a refreshing and nutritious start to your day.

Nutritional Information:

Per serving: 120 calories, 8g protein, 22g carbohydrates, 0.5g fat, 2g fiber, 5mg cholesterol, 30mg sodium, 250mg potassium, 100mg phosphorus.

10. Energizing Cranberry Walnut Toast

Yield: 2 servings | Prep time: 5 minutes | Cook time: 2 minutes

Ingredients:

- 2 slices low-sodium whole grain bread
- 2 tablespoons dried cranberries
- 2 tablespoons chopped walnuts

Directions:

1. Toast the whole grain bread slices to your preferred level of crispiness.
2. Evenly sprinkle the dried cranberries and chopped walnuts over the toasted bread slices.
3. Serve immediately, enjoying the crunchy, sweet, and nutty flavors.

Nutritional Information:

Per serving: 200 calories, 6g protein, 30g carbohydrates, 9g fat, 5g fiber, 0mg cholesterol, 120mg sodium, 150mg potassium, 100mg phosphorus.

11. Morning Harvest Veggie Egg Muffins

Yield: 6 servings | Prep time: 10 minutes | Cook time: 20 minutes

Ingredients:

- 8 large egg whites
- 1/2 cup chopped zucchini
- 1/2 cup diced red bell pepper
- 1 tablespoon chopped fresh herbs (such as parsley and chives)
- Cooking spray (for muffin tin)

Directions:

1. Preheat your oven to 350°F (175°C). Lightly grease a 6-cup muffin tin with cooking spray.
2. In a large bowl, whisk together the egg whites until frothy. Stir in the chopped zucchini, diced bell pepper, and fresh herbs.
3. Evenly divide the egg mixture among the prepared muffin cups.
4. Bake in the preheated oven for 20 minutes, or until the muffins are set and lightly golden on top.
5. Allow to cool slightly before removing from the muffin tin. Serve warm or at room temperature.

Nutritional Information:

Per serving: 60 calories, 7g protein, 3g carbohydrates, 0.5g fat, 1g fiber, 0mg cholesterol, 100mg sodium, 200mg potassium, 50mg phosphorus.

12. Sweet Morning Banana Pancakes

Yield: 4 servings | Prep time: 10 minutes | Cook time: 15 minutes

Ingredients:

- 2 medium ripe bananas, mashed
- 2 large eggs
- 1 cup all-purpose flour
- 2 teaspoons baking powder (aluminum-free)
- Honey, for serving

Directions:

1. In a large mixing bowl, combine the mashed bananas and eggs. Mix until well incorporated.
2. Sift the flour and baking powder into the banana and egg mixture. Stir until just combined; avoid overmixing to keep the pancakes fluffy.
3. Heat a non-stick skillet or griddle over medium heat. Lightly grease with cooking spray or a dab of butter if not strictly avoiding added fats.
4. Pour 1/4 cup of batter for each pancake onto the skillet. Cook until bubbles form on the surface and the edges look set, about 2-3 minutes. Flip and cook for another 2 minutes or until golden brown.
5. Serve the pancakes warm, drizzled with honey.

Nutritional Information:

Per serving: 220 calories, 6g protein, 45g carbohydrates, 2g fat, 3g fiber, 93mg cholesterol, 150mg sodium, 300mg potassium, 100mg phosphorus.

13. Lean Green Cheesy Spinach Omelet

Yield: 2 servings | Prep time: 5 minutes |
Cook time: 8 minutes

Ingredients:

- 6 large egg whites
- 2 cups fresh spinach, roughly chopped
- 1/2 cup shredded low-sodium cheese (e.g., mozzarella or Swiss)
- Cooking spray or a teaspoon of olive oil for the pan

Directions:

1. Lightly coat a non-stick skillet with cooking spray or olive oil and heat over medium heat.
2. Add the chopped spinach to the skillet and sauté for 2-3 minutes until wilted. Remove the spinach and set aside.
3. In the same skillet, pour in the egg whites. Cook for 1-2 minutes until they begin to set on the bottom.
4. Sprinkle the wilted spinach evenly over half of the omelet. Top the spinach with shredded cheese.
5. Carefully fold the other half of the omelet over the spinach and cheese. Continue cooking for another 2-3 minutes, or until the cheese is melted and the egg whites are fully set.
6. Slide the omelet onto a plate and serve immediately.

Nutritional Information:

Per serving: 180 calories, 20g protein,
3g carbohydrates, 8g fat, 1g fiber,
0mg cholesterol, 200mg sodium,
400mg potassium, 150mg phosphorus.

14. Blissful Berry Yogurt Parfait

Yield: 4 servings | Prep time: 10 minutes |
Cook time: 0 minutes

Ingredients:

- 2 cups low-phosphorus yogurt (e.g., Greek yogurt, unsweetened)
- 1 cup fresh mixed berries (strawberries, blueberries, raspberries)
- 1/2 cup low-sodium granola

Directions:

1. Begin by layering 1/4 cup of yogurt at the bottom of four glasses.
2. Add a layer of mixed berries (about 2 tablespoons per glass) on top of the yogurt.
3. Sprinkle a tablespoon of low-sodium granola over the berries.
4. Repeat the layering process until all ingredients are used, finishing with a layer of berries on top.
5. Serve immediately or refrigerate until ready to enjoy.

Nutritional Information:

Per serving: 180 calories, 10g protein,
25g carbohydrates, 4g fat, 3g fiber,
5mg cholesterol, 60mg sodium,
200mg potassium, 100mg phosphorus.

15. Hearty Morning Savory Oatmeal with Egg

Yield: 2 servings | Prep time: 5 minutes |
Cook time: 10 minutes

Ingredients:

- 1 cup low-phosphorus oatmeal (quick oats recommended)
- 2 cups water or low-sodium vegetable broth
- 2 large eggs
- 1 cup fresh spinach leaves
- Salt (optional) and pepper to taste

Directions:

1. Prepare the oatmeal according to package instructions using water or low-sodium vegetable broth for cooking. Season with a pinch of salt (if using) and pepper to taste.
2. While the oatmeal is cooking, poach the eggs. Bring a pot of water to a simmer, gently crack the eggs into the water, and cook for 3-4 minutes for a runny yolk or longer for a firmer yolk. Remove with a slotted spoon.
3. Steam the spinach briefly in a steamer or in the microwave until just wilted.
4. Divide the cooked oatmeal between two bowls. Top each bowl with a poached egg and half of the wilted spinach.
5. Serve immediately, seasoned with additional pepper to taste.

Nutritional Information:

Per serving: 250 calories, 12g protein, 35g carbohydrates, 7g fat, 5g fiber, 185mg cholesterol, 150mg sodium, 300mg potassium, 200mg phosphorus.

16. Golden Sunrise Tofu Scramble

Yield: 4 servings | Prep time: 10 minutes |
Cook time: 10 minutes

Ingredients:

- 1 block (14 oz) firm tofu, drained and pressed
- 1/2 teaspoon turmeric
- 1 bell pepper, diced
- 1 medium onion, diced
- 1 tablespoon olive oil
- Salt and pepper to taste (optional)

Directions:

1. Heat the olive oil in a large non-stick skillet over medium heat. Add the diced bell pepper and onion, sautéing until they are soft and lightly browned, about 5 minutes.
2. Crumble the tofu into the skillet with your hands, breaking it into bite-sized pieces.
3. Sprinkle the turmeric over the tofu and vegetables, stirring well to combine. The turmeric will give the tofu a vibrant, golden color and a boost of flavor.
4. Cook the mixture for another 5 minutes, stirring frequently, until the tofu is heated through and has absorbed the flavors of the turmeric and vegetables.
5. Season with salt and pepper to taste, if desired. Serve hot.

Nutritional Information:

Per serving: 150 calories, 12g protein, 8g carbohydrates, 9g fat, 2g fiber, 0mg cholesterol, 15mg sodium, 200mg potassium, 120mg phosphorus.

17. Morning Greens Kale and Mushroom Sauté

Yield: 4 servings | Prep time: 5 minutes | Cook time: 10 minutes

Ingredients:

- 4 cups chopped kale, stems removed
- 2 cups sliced mushrooms
- 2 cloves garlic, minced
- 2 tablespoons olive oil

Directions:

1. Heat the olive oil in a large skillet over medium heat. Add the minced garlic and sauté for about 1 minute until fragrant but not browned.
2. Increase the heat to medium-high and add the sliced mushrooms to the skillet. Sauté for 3-4 minutes until the mushrooms start to release their moisture and brown slightly.
3. Add the chopped kale to the skillet, stirring continuously. Cook for an additional 5-6 minutes, until the kale has wilted and is tender. If the mixture seems dry, add a tablespoon of water to help steam the kale.
4. Season with a pinch of salt and pepper to taste (optional), keeping the dish low in sodium.
5. Serve immediately as a nutritious side dish or a light main course.

Nutritional Information:

Per serving: 110 calories, 3g protein, 8g carbohydrates, 7g fat, 2g fiber, 0mg cholesterol, 30mg sodium, 200mg potassium, 50mg phosphorus..

18. Garden Fresh Zucchini Bread

Yield: 6 servings | Prep time: 15 minutes | Cook time: 50 minutes

Ingredients:

- 2 cups grated zucchini (about 2 medium zucchinis)
- 2 cups all-purpose flour
- 1 cup egg substitute
- 2 teaspoons baking powder (aluminum-free)
- Optional: A pinch of salt and spices like cinnamon or nutmeg to taste

Directions:

1. Preheat your oven to 350°F (175°C). Grease and flour a 9x5 inch loaf pan.
2. In a large bowl, combine the grated zucchini, flour, egg substitute, and baking powder. If using, add a pinch of salt and spices like cinnamon or nutmeg for flavor.
3. Mix until well combined. The batter will be quite thick.
4. Pour the batter into the prepared loaf pan, smoothing the top with a spatula.
5. Bake in the preheated oven for about 50 minutes, or until a toothpick inserted into the center of the loaf comes out clean.
6. Allow the bread to cool in the pan for 10 minutes, then turn out onto a wire rack to cool completely before slicing.

Nutritional Information:

Per serving: 200 calories, 8g protein, 40g carbohydrates, 1g fat, 2g fiber, 0mg cholesterol, 150mg sodium, 200mg potassium, 180mg phosphorus.

19. Honeyed Greek Yogurt with Almonds

Yield: 2 servings | Prep time: 5 minutes | Cook time: 0 minutes

Ingredients:

- 1 cup low-phosphorus Greek yogurt (unsweetened)
- 2 tablespoons honey
- 2 tablespoons sliced almonds

Directions:

1. Spoon the Greek yogurt into two serving bowls.
2. Drizzle each serving with 1 tablespoon of honey.
3. Sprinkle 1 tablespoon of sliced almonds over the top of each serving.
4. Serve immediately, enjoying the creamy texture of the yogurt with the sweetness of honey and the crunch of almonds.

Nutritional Information:

Per serving: 200 calories, 12g protein, 25g carbohydrates, 6g fat, 1g fiber, 10mg cholesterol, 50mg sodium, 200mg potassium, 150mg phosphorus.

20. Sunrise Quinoa Berry Bowl

Yield: 4 servings | Prep time: 10 minutes (assuming quinoa is precooked) | Cook time: 0 minutes

Ingredients:

- 2 cups cooked quinoa (cooled)
- 1/2 cup sliced almonds
- 1 cup mixed berries (blueberries, raspberries, strawberries)
- 1 cup unsweetened almond milk (or any preferred non-dairy milk)

Directions:

1. In a large bowl, combine the cooked quinoa with the almond milk and mix well.
2. Add the mixed berries to the quinoa mixture and gently fold them in to distribute evenly.
3. Sprinkle the sliced almonds over the top of the quinoa and berry mixture.
4. Divide the mixture into four serving bowls. This breakfast bowl can be enjoyed cold, or if preferred, gently heat the quinoa and almond milk mixture before adding the berries and almonds.

Nutritional Information:

Per serving: 250 calories, 9g protein, 38g carbohydrates, 9g fat, 6g fiber, 0mg cholesterol, 50mg sodium, 300mg potassium, 150mg phosphorus.

1. Quinoa Tabbouleh Twist

Yield: 4 servings | Prep time: 15 minutes | Cook time: 20 minutes (for quinoa)

Ingredients:

- 1 cup quinoa, rinsed
- 2 cups water
- 1 cup diced cucumber
- 1 cup diced tomatoes
- 1/2 cup chopped fresh parsley
- 2 tablespoons olive oil
- Juice of 1 lemon
- Salt and pepper to taste (keep salt minimal for low sodium)

Directions:

1. In a medium saucepan, bring 2 cups of water to a boil. Add the rinsed quinoa, reduce heat to low, cover, and simmer for about 15-20 minutes, or until the water is absorbed and quinoa is tender. Let cool.
2. In a large bowl, combine cooled quinoa, diced cucumber, diced tomatoes, and chopped parsley.
3. In a small bowl, whisk together olive oil, lemon juice, and a pinch of salt and pepper to create the lemon vinaigrette. Adjust seasoning to taste, keeping it renal-friendly.
4. Pour the vinaigrette over the quinoa mixture and toss to evenly coat.
5. Refrigerate for at least 1 hour before serving to allow flavors to meld. Serve chilled.

Nutritional Information:

Per serving: 220 calories, 6g protein, 30g carbohydrates, 10g fat, 5g fiber, 0mg cholesterol, 50mg sodium, 300mg potassium, 150mg phosphorus.

2. Lean & Green Turkey Avocado Wrap

Yield: 4 servings | Prep time: 10 minutes | Cook time: 0 minutes

Ingredients:

- 4 low-sodium whole wheat tortillas
- 8 ounces low-sodium sliced turkey breast
- 1 ripe avocado, sliced
- 2 cups fresh spinach leaves
- Optional: mustard or a low-sodium sauce for added flavor

Directions:

1. Lay out the whole wheat tortillas on a clean surface.
2. Evenly distribute the sliced turkey breast among the tortillas.
3. Add slices of avocado on top of the turkey.
4. Place a handful of fresh spinach leaves over the avocado on each tortilla.
5. If using, lightly spread a thin layer of mustard or low-sodium sauce over the fillings for extra flavor.
6. Carefully roll up the tortillas, folding in the sides as you go, to form a wrap.
7. Serve immediately, or wrap in foil to keep fresh if serving later.

Nutritional Information:

Per serving: 280 calories, 20g protein, 34g carbohydrates, 9g fat, 6g fiber, 30mg cholesterol, 200mg sodium, 400mg potassium, 100mg phosphorus.

3. Kidney Care Caprese Salad

Yield: 4 servings | Prep time: 10 minutes | Cook time: 0 minutes

Ingredients:

- 4 large ripe tomatoes, sliced
- 8 ounces low-moisture, part-skim mozzarella cheese, sliced
- 1/4 cup fresh basil leaves
- 2 tablespoons balsamic vinegar reduction (use a low-sodium balsamic glaze or reduce balsamic vinegar at home without adding salt)
- 1 tablespoon extra virgin olive oil
- Black pepper to taste

Directions:

1. Arrange slices of tomatoes and mozzarella cheese alternately on a serving platter, overlapping them for presentation.
2. Scatter fresh basil leaves over the top of the tomatoes and mozzarella slices.
3. Drizzle the balsamic vinegar reduction and extra virgin olive oil evenly over the salad.
4. Season with black pepper to taste. Serve immediately for the freshest flavor.

Nutritional Information:

Per serving: 220 calories, 14g protein, 9g carbohydrates, 16g fat, 2g fiber, 45mg cholesterol, 180mg sodium, 290mg potassium, 200mg phosphorus.

4. Hearty Veggie Stew

Yield: 4 servings | Prep time: 15 minutes | Cook time: 30 minutes

Ingredients:

- 2 cups low-sodium vegetable broth
- 1 cup diced carrots
- 1 cup diced celery
- 1 cup chopped green beans
- 1/2 cup diced onion
- 2 garlic cloves, minced
- 1 cup diced zucchini
- 1 cup cauliflower florets
- 1 teaspoon dried thyme
- 1 teaspoon dried oregano
- Black pepper to taste
- 2 tablespoons olive oil

Directions:

1. Heat olive oil in a large pot over medium heat. Add onion and garlic, and sauté until softened, about 3 minutes.
2. Add carrots, celery, and green beans to the pot. Cook for another 5 minutes, stirring occasionally.
3. Pour in the low-sodium vegetable broth and bring to a simmer. Add thyme, oregano, and black pepper. Cover and simmer for 10 minutes.
4. Add zucchini and cauliflower to the pot. Cover and simmer for another 10-15 minutes, or until all vegetables are tender.
5. Adjust seasoning to taste. Serve hot.

Nutritional Information:

Per serving: 120 calories, 3g protein, 18g carbohydrates, 5g fat, 5g fiber, 0mg cholesterol, 150mg sodium, 350mg potassium, 100mg phosphorus.

5. Refreshing Egg White Salad Sandwich

Yield: 4 servings | Prep time: 15 minutes | Cook time: 0 minutes (assuming egg whites are pre-cooked)

Ingredients:

- 8 large egg whites, hard-boiled and chopped
- 1/4 cup low-fat mayonnaise
- 2 tablespoons Dijon mustard
- 1/4 cup finely chopped celery
- Salt and pepper to taste (optional, keep minimal for low sodium)
- 8 slices low-sodium whole grain bread
- 1 cup lettuce leaves

Directions:

1. In a bowl, combine the chopped egg whites, low-fat mayonnaise, Dijon mustard, and chopped celery. Mix until well combined. Season with a pinch of salt and pepper if desired, keeping the dish low in sodium.
2. Take the low-sodium whole grain bread slices and lightly toast them if preferred.
3. Spread the egg white salad mixture evenly over 4 slices of bread. Top each with a few lettuce leaves.
4. Cover with the remaining bread slices to form sandwiches.
5. Cut each sandwich in half and serve immediately or wrap for a grab-and-go lunch option.

Nutritional Information:

Per serving: 250 calories, 20g protein, 30g carbohydrates, 5g fat, 5g fiber, 0mg cholesterol, 200mg sodium, 300mg potassium, 150mg phosphorus.

6. Simplified Dill Salmon Patties

Yield: 4 servings | Prep time: 15 minutes | Cook time: 10 minutes

Ingredients:

- 1 pound canned salmon, drained and flaked
- 1/4 cup breadcrumbs (use low-sodium, if available)
- 2 tablespoons fresh dill, chopped
- 1 egg, beaten (or equivalent egg substitute)
- 2 tablespoons olive oil for pan-frying
- Lemon wedges for serving

Directions:

1. In a mixing bowl, combine the flaked salmon, breadcrumbs, chopped dill, and beaten egg. Mix until well combined.
2. Form the mixture into 8 small patties.
3. Heat olive oil in a large non-stick skillet over medium heat.
4. Cook the salmon patties for about 5 minutes on each side, or until golden brown and cooked through.
5. Serve the patties hot with lemon wedges on the side.

Nutritional Information:

Per serving: 230 calories, 23g protein, 9g carbohydrates, 11g fat, 1g fiber, 60mg cholesterol, 190mg sodium, 350mg potassium, 250mg phosphorus.

7. Zesty Zucchini Noodles with Lemon-Herb Dressing

Yield: 4 servings | Prep time: 20 minutes | Cook time: 0 minutes

Ingredients:

- 4 medium zucchinis, spiralized into noodles
- 1 cup cherry tomatoes, halved
- 1/4 cup fresh lemon juice
- 2 tablespoons olive oil
- 1 tablespoon fresh chopped basil
- 1 tablespoon fresh chopped parsley
- Salt (optional) and pepper to taste
- Lemon zest for garnish

Directions:

1. Place the spiralized zucchini noodles in a large bowl.
2. In a small bowl, whisk together lemon juice, olive oil, basil, parsley, and a pinch of pepper. Adjust the seasoning according to taste, being mindful of sodium intake.
3. Pour the lemon-herb dressing over the zucchini noodles and toss gently to coat.
4. Add the halved cherry tomatoes to the zucchini noodles and toss again lightly.
5. Serve the zesty zucchini noodles immediately, garnished with lemon zest for an extra pop of flavor.

Nutritional Information:

Per serving: 120 calories, 3g protein, 10g carbohydrates, 7g fat, 3g fiber, 0mg cholesterol, 30mg sodium, 400mg potassium, 100mg phosphorus.

8. Soothing Mushroom Soup

Yield: 4 servings | Prep time: 15 minutes | Cook time: 30 minutes

Ingredients:

- 2 tablespoons olive oil
- 1 cup diced onions
- 2 cloves garlic, minced
- 2 cups sliced fresh mushrooms (button or cremini)
- 4 cups low-sodium vegetable broth
- 1 teaspoon dried thyme
- Salt (optional) and pepper to taste
- 2 tablespoons chopped fresh parsley for garnish

Directions:

1. Heat olive oil in a large pot over medium heat. Add onions and garlic, sautéing until onions are translucent, about 5 minutes.
2. Add the sliced mushrooms to the pot, and continue to sauté until mushrooms are soft and their liquid has evaporated, about 10 minutes.
3. Pour in the low-sodium vegetable broth and bring the mixture to a simmer. Add dried thyme and a pinch of pepper. Reduce heat, cover, and simmer for 15 minutes.
4. Taste the soup and adjust seasoning with a pinch of salt (if using) and more pepper as needed.
5. Serve the soup hot, garnished with fresh parsley.

Nutritional Information:

Per serving: 100 calories, 3g protein, 10g carbohydrates, 5g fat, 2g fiber, 0mg cholesterol, 100mg sodium, 300mg potassium, 90mg phosphorus.

9. Tuna Salad Scoop in Lettuce Cups

Yield: 4 servings | Prep time: 10 minutes | Cook time: 0 minutes

Ingredients:

- 2 cans (5 ounces each) low-sodium tuna, drained
- 1/4 cup low-sodium mayonnaise
- 2 tablespoons finely chopped celery
- 2 tablespoons finely chopped red onion
- 1 tablespoon lemon juice
- Black pepper to taste
- 8 large lettuce leaves (e.g., butter lettuce or romaine hearts) for serving

Directions:

1. In a mixing bowl, combine the drained tuna, low-sodium mayonnaise, chopped celery, chopped red onion, and lemon juice. Mix until well combined.
2. Season the tuna mixture with black pepper to taste, mixing thoroughly.
3. Carefully wash and dry the lettuce leaves. Place them on a serving platter.
4. Scoop an equal portion of the tuna salad into each lettuce leaf, creating lettuce cups.
5. Serve immediately, offering a refreshing and healthy take on the traditional tuna salad.

Nutritional Information:

Per serving: 150 calories, 20g protein, 4g carbohydrates, 6g fat, 1g fiber, 30mg cholesterol, 150mg sodium, 200mg potassium, 100mg phosphorus.

10. Balsamic Glazed Chicken Breast

Yield: 4 servings | Prep time: 15 minutes | Cook time: 25 minutes

Ingredients:

- 4 boneless, skinless chicken breasts
- 1/2 cup balsamic vinegar
- 2 cloves garlic, minced
- 1 tablespoon olive oil
- Salt (optional) and pepper to taste
- Fresh herbs for garnish (e.g., rosemary or thyme)

Directions:

1. In a small saucepan, bring balsamic vinegar to a boil over medium heat. Reduce heat and simmer until the vinegar thickens and reduces to about a quarter of its original volume, approximately 15 minutes. Stir in minced garlic.
2. While the balsamic reduction is simmering, season chicken breasts with a pinch of pepper (and salt if using, though keep minimal for a low-sodium diet).
3. Heat olive oil in a grill pan over medium-high heat. Add chicken breasts and cook for about 6-7 minutes on each side, or until the internal temperature reaches 165°F (74°C) and juices run clear.
4. Once the chicken is cooked, remove from heat and let it rest for a few minutes. Drizzle the balsamic reduction over the chicken breasts.
5. Garnish with fresh herbs before serving.

Nutritional Information:

Per serving: 220 calories, 26g protein, 9g carbohydrates, 7g fat, 0g fiber, 65mg cholesterol, 70mg sodium, 250mg potassium, 200mg phosphorus.

11. Crisp Cucumber Cream Cheese Sandwiches

Yield: 4 servings | Prep time: 10 minutes | Cook time: 0 minutes

Ingredients:

- 8 slices low-sodium whole grain bread
- 1/2 cup low-fat cream cheese, softened
- 1 large cucumber, thinly sliced
- Fresh dill (optional) for garnish

Directions:

1. Spread each slice of bread with a thin layer of low-fat cream cheese.
2. Arrange cucumber slices evenly over four of the bread slices. If desired, add a sprinkle of fresh dill for extra flavor.
3. Top with the remaining slices of bread, cream cheese side down, to form sandwiches.
4. Cut each sandwich into halves or quarters, depending on preference.
5. Serve immediately for the freshest taste.

Nutritional Information:

Per serving: 200 calories, 8g protein, 28g carbohydrates, 6g fat, 4g fiber, 15mg cholesterol, 150mg sodium, 200mg potassium, 100mg phosphorus.

12. Crisp Kale and Apple Salad with Walnuts

Yield: 4 servings | Prep time: 15 minutes | Cook time: 0 minutes

Ingredients:

- 4 cups chopped kale, stems removed
- 1 large apple, cored and thinly sliced
- 1/2 cup walnuts, roughly chopped
- 2 tablespoons olive oil
- Juice of 1 lemon
- Salt (optional) and pepper to taste
- 1 teaspoon honey (optional, for sweetness)

Directions:

1. In a large bowl, combine the chopped kale and lemon juice. Massage the kale with your hands for about 2 minutes to soften the leaves.
2. Add the olive oil, a pinch of salt (if using), pepper, and honey to the kale. Toss well to coat evenly.
3. Add the sliced apple and chopped walnuts to the bowl. Toss gently to combine all the ingredients.
4. Let the salad sit for about 5 minutes before serving to allow flavors to meld.
5. Serve as a refreshing side dish or a light meal.

Nutritional Information:

Per serving: 220 calories, 5g protein, 20g carbohydrates, 15g fat, 4g fiber, 0mg cholesterol, 50mg sodium, 300mg potassium, 150mg phosphorus.

13. Herb-Infused Roasted Cauliflower Steaks

Yield: 4 servings | Prep time: 10 minutes | Cook time: 25 minutes

Ingredients:

- 1 large head of cauliflower, sliced into 4 steaks
- 2 tablespoons olive oil
- 1 teaspoon dried thyme
- 1 teaspoon dried rosemary
- Salt (optional) and pepper to taste

Directions:

1. Preheat the oven to 400°F (200°C). Line a baking sheet with parchment paper.
2. Carefully slice the cauliflower head vertically into 4 thick steaks. Place the cauliflower steaks on the prepared baking sheet.
3. Brush both sides of each cauliflower steak with olive oil. Sprinkle the dried thyme, rosemary, and a pinch of pepper (and salt if using, though keep minimal for a low-sodium diet) over the steaks.
4. Roast in the preheated oven for about 25 minutes, or until the cauliflower is tender and the edges are golden brown, flipping halfway through cooking.
5. Serve the roasted cauliflower steaks hot, garnished with additional herbs if desired.

Nutritional Information:

Per serving: 120 calories, 4g protein, 11g carbohydrates, 7g fat, 5g fiber, 0mg cholesterol, 30mg sodium, 450mg potassium, 75mg phosphorus.

14. Zesty Lemon Pepper Tilapia

Yield: 4 servings | Prep time: 10 minutes | Cook time: 10 minutes

Ingredients:

- 4 tilapia fillets (about 6 ounces each)
- 2 tablespoons olive oil
- Juice of 1 lemon
- 1 teaspoon ground black pepper
- 1/2 teaspoon garlic powder
- Salt to taste (optional, minimal use for low sodium)
- Lemon slices and fresh parsley for garnish

Directions:

1. Preheat a grill or grill pan over medium heat. Brush the grill surface with a bit of olive oil to prevent sticking.
2. In a small bowl, mix olive oil, lemon juice, black pepper, and garlic powder. Brush this mixture on both sides of the tilapia fillets. Season with a pinch of salt if desired.
3. Place tilapia fillets on the grill. Cook for about 4-5 minutes on each side, or until the fish flakes easily with a fork.
4. Remove the fillets from the grill and place them on a serving platter. Garnish with lemon slices and fresh parsley.
5. Serve immediately with a side of steamed vegetables or a salad for a complete meal.

Nutritional Information:

Per serving: 180 calories, 23g protein, 0g carbohydrates, 10g fat, 0g fiber, 55mg cholesterol, 50mg sodium, 350mg potassium, 200mg phosphorus.

15. Crispy Chickpea Salad

Yield: 4 servings | Prep time: 10 minutes |
Cook time: 30 minutes (for chickpeas)

Ingredients:

- 1 can (15 ounces) low-sodium chickpeas, drained, rinsed, and patted dry
- 1 tablespoon olive oil
- 1/2 teaspoon garlic powder
- 4 cups mixed greens (lettuce, spinach, arugula)
- 1/2 cup cherry tomatoes, halved
- 1/4 cup sliced cucumber
- 1/4 cup red onion, thinly sliced
- 2 tablespoons balsamic vinegar
- 1 tablespoon extra virgin olive oil
- Pepper to taste

Directions:

1. Preheat the oven to 400°F (200°C). Toss the chickpeas with 1 tablespoon olive oil and garlic powder. Spread them on a baking sheet and roast for 25-30 minutes, stirring halfway through, until crispy.
2. While the chickpeas are roasting, prepare the salad by combining mixed greens, cherry tomatoes, cucumber, and red onion in a large bowl.
3. In a small bowl, whisk together balsamic vinegar and extra virgin olive oil for the dressing. Season with pepper to taste.
4. Once the chickpeas are crispy, let them cool for a few minutes.
5. Add the roasted chickpeas to the salad. Drizzle with the balsamic dressing and toss gently to combine.
6. Serve the salad immediately for the best texture of the chickpeas.

Nutritional Information:

Per serving: 200 calories, 7g protein,
22g carbohydrates, 10g fat, 6g fiber,
0mg cholesterol, 100mg sodium,
300mg potassium, 150mg phosphorus.

16. Herbed Grilled Veggie Platter

Yield: 4 servings | Prep time: 15 minutes |
Cook time: 20 minutes

Ingredients:

- 2 zucchinis, sliced lengthwise
- 2 yellow squash, sliced lengthwise
- 1 red bell pepper, seeded and quartered
- 1 yellow bell pepper, seeded and quartered
- 1 eggplant, sliced into rounds
- 2 tablespoons olive oil
- 1 teaspoon dried oregano
- 1 teaspoon dried thyme
- Pepper to taste

Directions:

1. Preheat the grill to medium-high heat.
2. In a large bowl, toss the sliced zucchinis, yellow squash, bell peppers, and eggplant with olive oil, oregano, thyme, and pepper until evenly coated.
3. Place the vegetables on the grill in a single layer. Grill for about 10 minutes, turning once, or until the vegetables are tender and have grill marks.
4. Remove the vegetables from the grill and arrange them on a serving platter.
5. Serve the grilled veggies hot or at room temperature, garnished with fresh herbs if desired.

Nutritional Information:

Per serving: 150 calories, 3g protein,
18g carbohydrates, 7g fat, 6g fiber,
0mg cholesterol, 30mg sodium,
400mg potassium, 100mg phosphorus.

17. Avocado Chicken Wrap

Yield: 4 servings | Prep time: 20 minutes | Cook time: 0 minutes (assuming chicken is pre-cooked)

Ingredients:

- 2 cups shredded cooked chicken breast
- 1 ripe avocado, mashed
- 1/2 cup shredded low-sodium cheese (such as mozzarella or Swiss)
- 4 low-sodium whole wheat tortillas
- 1 cup spinach leaves
- 1/4 cup diced tomatoes (optional)
- 1 tablespoon lime juice
- Pepper to taste

Directions:

1. In a bowl, mix the shredded chicken with mashed avocado, lime juice, and a pinch of pepper. Stir until well combined.
2. Lay out the whole wheat tortillas on a flat surface. Evenly distribute the chicken and avocado mixture onto each tortilla.
3. Sprinkle the shredded low-sodium cheese over the chicken mixture.
4. Add a layer of spinach leaves and diced tomatoes (if using) on top.
5. Carefully roll each tortilla, folding in the sides to enclose the filling.
6. Serve immediately, or if preferred, lightly grill the wraps on a pan for 1-2 minutes on each side to warm through.

Nutritional Information:

Per serving: 300 calories, 25g protein, 27g carbohydrates, 12g fat, 5g fiber, 60mg cholesterol, 200mg sodium, 350mg potassium, 150mg phosphorus.

18. Whole Wheat Broccoli and Cheese Pasta

Yield: 4 servings | Prep time: 15 minutes | Cook time: 20 minutes

Ingredients:

- 8 ounces whole wheat pasta
- 2 cups fresh broccoli florets
- 2 tablespoons olive oil
- 2 cloves garlic, minced
- 1 cup low-sodium, low-phosphorus cheese (e.g., ricotta or mozzarella), grated
- 1/2 cup low-sodium vegetable broth
- Pepper to taste
- Fresh parsley for garnish

Directions:

1. Cook the whole wheat pasta according to package instructions until al dente. Drain and set aside, reserving 1/2 cup of pasta water.
2. While the pasta is cooking, steam the broccoli florets until tender, about 5 minutes. Set aside.
3. In the same pot used for pasta, heat olive oil over medium heat. Add minced garlic and sauté for 1-2 minutes until fragrant.
4. Reduce heat to low and add the low-sodium cheese and vegetable broth to the pot, stirring until the cheese is melted and the sauce is smooth. If the sauce is too thick, add a little reserved pasta water until you reach the desired consistency.
5. Add the cooked pasta and steamed broccoli to the pot, tossing to coat evenly with the cheese sauce.
6. Season with pepper to taste and garnish with fresh parsley before serving.

Nutritional Information:

Per serving: 350 calories, 15g protein, 45g carbohydrates, 12g fat, 7g fiber, 20mg cholesterol, 200mg sodium, 400mg potassium, 250mg phosphorus.

19. Hearty Savory Lentil Soup

Yield: 4 servings | Prep time: 10 minutes |
Cook time: 45 minutes

Ingredients:

- 1 cup dried lentils, rinsed
- 4 cups low-sodium vegetable broth
- 1 cup water
- 1 medium carrot, diced
- 1 stalk celery, diced
- 1 small onion, diced
- 2 cloves garlic, minced
- 1 teaspoon dried thyme
- 1 teaspoon dried rosemary
- Pepper to taste
- 1 tablespoon olive oil

Directions:

1. In a large pot, heat olive oil over medium heat. Add the onion, carrot, and celery. Sauté until the vegetables are softened, about 5 minutes.
2. Add the minced garlic, thyme, and rosemary. Cook for another minute until fragrant.
3. Pour in the low-sodium vegetable broth and water. Bring to a boil.
4. Add the rinsed lentils to the pot. Reduce heat to a simmer, cover, and cook for 35-40 minutes, or until the lentils are tender.
5. Season with pepper to taste. Adjust the consistency with more water if desired.
6. Serve hot, garnished with a sprinkle of fresh herbs if available.

Nutritional Information:

Per serving: 250 calories, 15g protein, 40g carbohydrates, 4g fat, 15g fiber, 0mg cholesterol, 100mg sodium, 350mg potassium, 150mg phosphorus.

20. Bright Mediterranean Chickpea Salad

Yield: 4 servings | Prep time: 15 minutes |
Cook time: 0 minutes

Ingredients:

- 2 cups cooked chickpeas (low-sodium canned, rinsed, and drained)
- 1 cup cucumber, diced
- 1/2 cup Kalamata olives, halved
- 1/2 cup low-sodium feta cheese, crumbled
- 1/4 cup red onion, thinly sliced
- 2 tablespoons extra virgin olive oil
- Juice of 1 lemon
- 1 teaspoon dried oregano
- Pepper to taste
- Fresh parsley, chopped, for garnish

Directions:

1. In a large bowl, combine the chickpeas, cucumber, Kalamata olives, crumbled feta cheese, and red onion.
2. In a small bowl, whisk together the extra virgin olive oil, lemon juice, dried oregano, and pepper to create the dressing.
3. Pour the dressing over the salad and toss gently to ensure all ingredients are evenly coated.
4. Let the salad sit for at least 10 minutes to allow the flavors to meld together.
5. Garnish with chopped fresh parsley before serving.

Nutritional Information:

Per serving: 280 calories, 10g protein, 30g carbohydrates, 14g fat, 8g fiber, 15mg cholesterol, 200mg sodium, 400mg potassium, 150mg phosphorus.

Dinnertime Dreams: 22 Recipes for Memorable Evenings

1. Lemon-Dill Salmon

Yield: 4 servings | Prep time: 10 minutes | Cook time: 20 minutes

Ingredients:

- 4 salmon fillets (about 6 ounces each)
- 2 tablespoons olive oil
- Juice of 1 lemon
- 1 tablespoon fresh dill, chopped
- Freshly ground black pepper to taste
- Lemon slices and additional dill for garnish

Directions:

1. Preheat the oven to 375°F (190°C). Line a baking sheet with parchment paper for easy cleanup.
2. Place the salmon fillets on the prepared baking sheet. Brush each fillet with olive oil.
3. Squeeze fresh lemon juice evenly over the salmon fillets. Sprinkle with chopped dill and add freshly ground black pepper to taste.
4. Bake in the preheated oven for about 15-20 minutes, or until the salmon flakes easily with a fork.
5. Serve the salmon garnished with lemon slices and a sprinkle of additional dill.

Nutritional Information:

Per serving: 280 calories, 25g protein, 0g carbohydrates, 20g fat, 0g fiber, 65mg cholesterol, 70mg sodium, 500mg potassium, 250mg phosphorus.

2. Garlic Butter Shrimp

Yield: 4 servings | Prep time: 10 minutes | Cook time: 10 minutes

Ingredients:

- 1 pound large shrimp, peeled and deveined
- 4 tablespoons unsalted butter
- 4 cloves garlic, minced
- Juice of 1 lemon
- 1 tablespoon chopped parsley
- Freshly ground black pepper to taste
- Lemon wedges for serving

Directions:

1. Melt the unsalted butter in a large skillet over medium heat. Add the minced garlic and sauté for 1-2 minutes until fragrant but not browned.
2. Increase the heat to medium-high and add the shrimp to the skillet. Cook for 2-3 minutes on each side, or until the shrimp are pink and opaque.
3. Squeeze lemon juice over the cooked shrimp and stir to combine. Season with freshly ground black pepper to taste.
4. Remove from heat and sprinkle chopped parsley over the shrimp.
5. Serve immediately with lemon wedges on the side.

Nutritional Information:

Per serving: 230 calories, 24g protein, 1g carbohydrates, 14g fat, 0g fiber, 220mg cholesterol, 85mg sodium, 200mg potassium, 250mg phosphorus.

3. Roasted Turkey Breast with Thyme

Yield: 4 servings | Prep time: 15 minutes |
Cook time: 60 minutes

Ingredients:

- 2 pounds turkey breast
- 2 tablespoons olive oil
- 1 tablespoon fresh thyme, chopped
- Freshly ground black pepper to taste
- 2 cups green beans, trimmed
- 1 tablespoon unsalted butter (for green beans)

Directions:

1. Preheat the oven to 350°F (175°C). Place the turkey breast in a roasting pan.
2. Rub the turkey breast with olive oil. Sprinkle the chopped thyme and black pepper over the turkey.
3. Roast the turkey in the preheated oven for about 60 minutes, or until the internal temperature reaches 165°F (74°C). Baste occasionally with the pan juices.
4. About 20 minutes before the turkey is done, steam the green beans until tender, about 5-7 minutes. Toss the steamed green beans with unsalted butter and a pinch of pepper.
5. Let the turkey rest for 10 minutes after removing it from the oven. Slice and serve with the steamed green beans on the side.

Nutritional Information:

Per serving: 300 calories, 35g protein, 4g carbohydrates, 16g fat, 2g fiber, 85mg cholesterol, 100mg sodium, 350mg potassium, 250mg phosphorus.

4. Balsamic Glazed Beef

Yield: 4 servings | Prep time: 15 minutes |
Cook time: 25 minutes

Ingredients:

- 1 pound lean beef tenderloin, cut into 4 steaks
- 1/2 cup balsamic vinegar
- 2 cloves garlic, minced
- 1 teaspoon honey
- 1 tablespoon olive oil
- Freshly ground black pepper to taste
- Fresh thyme or rosemary for garnish

Directions:

1. In a small saucepan, combine the balsamic vinegar, minced garlic, and honey. Bring to a simmer over medium heat and reduce by half until thickened into a glaze, about 10-15 minutes. Set aside.
2. Heat olive oil in a large skillet over medium-high heat. Season the beef steaks with freshly ground black pepper.
3. Sear the steaks in the skillet for about 4-5 minutes on each side for medium-rare, or until desired doneness.
4. Remove the steaks from the skillet and let them rest for a few minutes.
5. Drizzle the reduced balsamic glaze over the steaks just before serving. Garnish with fresh thyme or rosemary.
6. Serve with a side of steamed vegetables or a salad for a complete meal.

Nutritional Information:

Per serving: 250 calories, 24g protein, 8g carbohydrates, 12g fat, 0g fiber, 60mg cholesterol, 80mg sodium, 300mg potassium, 200mg phosphorus.

5. Cauliflower Steak with Herb Sauce

Yield: 4 servings | Prep time: 15 minutes |
Cook time: 25 minutes

Ingredients:

- 2 large heads of cauliflower
- 2 tablespoons olive oil
- For the Herb Sauce:
- 1/4 cup olive oil
- 2 tablespoons lemon juice
- 1 tablespoon fresh parsley, finely chopped
- 1 tablespoon fresh chives, finely chopped
- 1 clove garlic, minced
- Freshly ground black pepper to taste

Directions:

1. Preheat the oven to 400°F (200°C) or preheat your grill to medium-high heat.
2. Remove the leaves from the cauliflower and cut the heads into 1-inch thick steaks. You should get about 2 steaks per head, depending on size.
3. Brush each cauliflower steak on both sides with olive oil. Place on a baking sheet lined with parchment paper if baking, or directly on the grill.
4. Roast or grill the cauliflower steaks for about 12-15 minutes on each side, until they are golden brown and tender.
5. While the cauliflower cooks, prepare the herb sauce. In a small bowl, whisk together the olive oil, lemon juice, parsley, chives, minced garlic, and black pepper.
6. Once the cauliflower steaks are cooked, transfer them to serving plates. Drizzle the herb sauce over the steaks just before serving.

Nutritional Information:

Per serving: 210 calories, 4g protein,
11g carbohydrates, 18g fat, 5g fiber,
0mg cholesterol, 45mg sodium,
500mg potassium, 150mg phosphorus.

6. Pork Tenderloin with Apple Compote

Yield: 4 servings | Prep time: 15 minutes |
Cook time: 30 minutes

Ingredients:

- 1 pork tenderloin (about 1 pound)
- 2 tablespoons olive oil
- Freshly ground black pepper to taste
- For the Apple Compote:
- 2 medium apples, peeled, cored, and diced
- 1/4 cup water
- 1 tablespoon lemon juice
- 1 teaspoon cinnamon
- 1 tablespoon honey or a sugar substitute suitable for a renal diet

Directions:

1. Preheat the oven to 375°F (190°C). Season the pork tenderloin with black pepper.
2. Heat 1 tablespoon of olive oil in a skillet over medium-high heat. Sear the pork tenderloin on all sides until golden brown, about 5-7 minutes.
3. Transfer the pork to a baking dish and roast in the preheated oven for about 20-25 minutes, or until the internal temperature reaches 145°F (63°C). Let it rest for 5 minutes before slicing.
4. While the pork is roasting, make the apple compote. Combine the diced apples, water, lemon juice, cinnamon, and honey in a saucepan over medium heat.
5. Cook the compote, stirring occasionally, until the apples are soft and the mixture has thickened, about 15-20 minutes.
6. Slice the rested pork tenderloin and serve with the warm apple compote on the side.

Nutritional Information:

Per serving: 250 calories, 24g protein,
15g carbohydrates, 10g fat, 2g fiber,
65mg cholesterol, 45mg sodium,
350mg potassium, 200mg phosphorus.

7. Spinach and Goat Cheese Stuffed Chicken

Yield: 4 servings | Prep time: 20 minutes | Cook time: 25 minutes

Ingredients:

- 4 boneless, skinless chicken breasts
- 4 ounces low-sodium goat cheese
- 2 cups fresh spinach, sautéed and cooled
- 1 tablespoon olive oil
- Freshly ground black pepper to taste
- Toothpicks or kitchen twine to secure
- Fresh herbs (such as thyme or rosemary) for garnish

Directions:

1. Preheat the oven to 375°F (190°C).
2. Flatten the chicken breasts to about 1/4 inch thickness using a meat mallet.
3. Spread each chicken breast with an ounce of low-sodium goat cheese and a layer of sautéed spinach.
4. Carefully roll up the chicken breasts and secure them with toothpicks or kitchen twine.
5. Season the outside of the chicken rolls with freshly ground black pepper.
6. Heat olive oil in a large, oven-safe skillet over medium-high heat. Sear the chicken rolls on all sides until golden brown, about 3-4 minutes in total.
7. Transfer the skillet to the preheated oven and bake for 20 minutes, or until the chicken reaches an internal temperature of 165°F (74°C).
8. Let the chicken rest for a few minutes before removing the toothpicks or twine. Slice into medallions and garnish with fresh herbs before serving.

Nutritional Information:

Per serving: 280 calories, 30g protein, 3g carbohydrates, 16g fat, 1g fiber, 75mg cholesterol, 150mg sodium, 400mg potassium, 250mg phosphorus.

8. Grilled Portobello Mushrooms

Yield: 4 servings | Prep time: 10 minutes | Cook time: 10 minutes

Ingredients:

- 4 large portobello mushroom caps
- 2 tablespoons olive oil
- 2 cloves garlic, minced
- Freshly ground black pepper to taste
- Fresh herbs (such as thyme or parsley) for garnish

Directions:

1. Preheat your grill to medium-high heat.
2. Gently clean the portobello mushrooms with a damp cloth and remove the stems. Using a spoon, scrape out the gills from the underside of the mushrooms if desired.
3. In a small bowl, mix together the olive oil and minced garlic. Brush this mixture over both sides of the mushroom caps.
4. Season the mushrooms with freshly ground black pepper to taste.
5. Place the mushrooms on the grill, cap side down, and grill for about 5 minutes. Flip the mushrooms and grill for another 5 minutes, or until they are tender and have grill marks.
6. Serve the grilled mushrooms garnished with fresh herbs.

Nutritional Information:

Per serving: 80 calories, 2g protein, 4g carbohydrates, 7g fat, 1g fiber, 0mg cholesterol, 5mg sodium, 300mg potassium, 50mg phosphorus.

9. Tuna Nicoise Salad

Yield: 4 servings | Prep time: 20 minutes |
Cook time: 10 minutes

Ingredients:

- 8 ounces low-sodium canned tuna, drained
- 1 pound fresh green beans, trimmed
- 4 hard-boiled eggs, quartered
- 2 medium potatoes, boiled and sliced
- 1/4 cup olives, sliced (optional, ensure they are low in sodium)
- For the Vinaigrette:
- 3 tablespoons olive oil
- 1 tablespoon lemon juice
- 1 teaspoon Dijon mustard (check for low sodium)
- 1 small garlic clove, minced
- Freshly ground black pepper to taste

Directions:

1. Blanche the green beans in boiling water for 3-4 minutes until bright green and tender-crisp. Drain and plunge into ice water to stop the cooking process. Drain again and set aside.
2. Arrange the sliced potatoes on a large platter as the salad base.
3. Scatter the blanched green beans, quartered hard-boiled eggs, and olives (if using) over the potatoes.
4. Flake the low-sodium tuna and distribute it evenly atop the salad.
5. Prepare the vinaigrette by whisking together olive oil, lemon juice, Dijon mustard, minced garlic, and black pepper in a small bowl.
6. Drizzle the vinaigrette over the salad just before serving.

Nutritional Information:

Per serving: 320 calories, 25g protein, 20g carbohydrates, 18g fat, 5g fiber, 190mg cholesterol, 200mg sodium, 600mg potassium, 250mg phosphorus.

10. Chicken Piccata Light

Yield: 4 servings | Prep time: 15 minutes |
Cook time: 20 minutes

Ingredients:

- 4 boneless, skinless chicken breasts, pounded to even thickness
- 2 tablespoons all-purpose flour (for dusting)
- 2 tablespoons olive oil
- Juice of 1 large lemon
- 1/2 cup low-sodium chicken broth
- 1 tablespoon capers, rinsed
- 1 tablespoon unsalted butter
- Fresh parsley, chopped, for garnish
- Freshly ground black pepper to taste

Directions:

1. Lightly dust the chicken breasts with flour, shaking off any excess.
2. Heat olive oil in a large skillet over medium-high heat. Add the chicken and cook until golden brown on both sides and cooked through, about 4-5 minutes per side. Remove the chicken from the skillet and set aside.
3. To the same skillet, add the lemon juice, low-sodium chicken broth, and capers. Bring to a simmer, scraping up any browned bits from the bottom of the skillet.
4. Simmer the sauce for about 3 minutes, or until it has slightly thickened. Remove from heat and whisk in the unsalted butter until the sauce is smooth and glossy.
5. Return the chicken to the skillet and spoon the sauce over the top.
6. Garnish with chopped parsley and freshly ground black pepper before serving.

Nutritional Information:

Per serving: 220 calories, 26g protein, 5g carbohydrates, 11g fat, 0g fiber, 75mg cholesterol, 150mg sodium, 300mg potassium, 200mg phosphorus

11. Vegetable Stir-Fry with Tofu

Yield: 4 servings | Prep time: 15 minutes | Cook time: 10 minutes

Ingredients:

- 14 ounces firm tofu, drained and cubed
- 2 tablespoons olive oil
- 1 cup sliced bell peppers (red and yellow)
- 1 cup broccoli florets
- 1/2 cup sliced carrots and 1/2 cup snow peas
- 2 garlic cloves, minced
- For the sauce:
- 2 tablespoons low-sodium soy sauce
- 1 tablespoon rice vinegar, sesame oil, honey, cornstarch (mixed with 1 tablespoon water)
- Freshly ground black pepper to taste
- Sesame seeds for garnish

Directions:

1. Press the tofu to remove excess water, then cut into cubes. Brown in 1 tbsp oil. Set aside.
2. In the same skillet, add the remaining olive oil, bell peppers, broccoli, carrots, snow peas, and minced garlic. Stir-fry the vegetables for about 5 minutes.
3. Whisk together the low-sodium soy sauce, rice vinegar, sesame oil, honey, and cornstarch mixture in a small bowl.
4. Return the tofu to the skillet with the vegetables. Pour the sauce over the tofu and vegetables, stirring to combine. Cook for an additional 2 minutes, or until the sauce has thickened and everything is heated through.
5. Season with freshly ground black pepper. Garnish with sesam.

Nutritional Information:

Per serving: 220 calories, 12g protein, 15g carbohydrates, 12g fat, 3g fiber, 0mg cholesterol, 200mg sodium, 400mg potassium, 150mg phosphorus.

12. Creamy Low-Potassium Mushroom Risotto

Yield: 4 servings | Prep time: 10 minutes | Cook time: 30 minutes

Ingredients:

- 1 cup arborio rice
- 2 tablespoons olive oil
- 1 small onion, finely chopped
- 2 cloves garlic, minced
- 2 cups low-potassium mushrooms, sliced
- 4 cups low-sodium vegetable broth, warmed
- 1/2 cup white wine (optional)
- Black pepper to taste
- 1/4 cup low-sodium grated Parmesan cheese
- Fresh parsley, for garnish

Directions:

1. Heat oil in a pan. Sauté onion and garlic until soft.
2. Add mushrooms; cook until they begin to soften.
3. Mix in rice, stir for 2 minutes.
4. Pour in wine if using, let it absorb.
5. Add broth gradually, allow each addition to absorb before adding more, until rice is creamy and cooked, about 20-25 minutes.
6. Off heat, stir in Parmesan and pepper.
7. Garnish with parsley and serve.

Nutritional Information:

Per serving: 320 calories, 8g protein, 45g carbohydrates, 10g fat, 2g fiber, 10mg cholesterol, 150mg sodium, 300mg potassium, 150mg phosphorus..

13. Zucchini Lasagna

Yield: 4 servings | Prep time: 20 minutes | Cook time: 45 minutes

Ingredients:

- 3 large zucchinis, sliced lengthwise
- 1 lb ground turkey
- 1 tbsp olive oil
- 1 small onion, chopped
- 2 cloves garlic, minced
- 1 cup low-sodium tomato sauce
- 1 tsp each of oregano and basil
- 1 cup low-sodium ricotta
- 1 egg
- 1 cup low-sodium mozzarella, shredded
- Black pepper to taste
- Fresh basil for garnish

Directions:

1. Preheat oven to 375°F. Grease a baking dish.
2. Cook onion, garlic, and turkey in olive oil until browned. Add tomato sauce, herbs, and pepper. Simmer for 10 minutes.
3. Mix ricotta with egg.
4. Layer zucchini, turkey mixture, and ricotta in the dish, ending with zucchini.
5. Top with mozzarella and bake covered for 30 mins. Uncover and bake 15 more mins until golden.
6. Rest for 10 mins, garnish with basil.

Nutritional Information:

Per serving: 350 calories, 28g protein, 15g carbohydrates, 20g fat, 4g fiber, 115mg cholesterol, 200mg sodium, 400mg potassium, 250mg phosphorus.

14. Eggplant Parmesan Light

Yield: 4 servings | Prep time: 15 minutes | Cook time: 45 minutes

Ingredients:

- 2 medium eggplants, sliced into 1/2-inch thick rounds
- 2 tablespoons olive oil
- 2 cups low-sodium tomato sauce
- 1 cup shredded mozzarella cheese (low-sodium)
- 1/4 cup grated Parmesan cheese (low-sodium)
- 1 teaspoon dried oregano
- 1 teaspoon dried basil
- Freshly ground black pepper to taste
- Fresh basil leaves for garnish

Directions:

1. Preheat the oven to 375°F (190°C). Line two baking sheets with parchment paper.
2. Arrange eggplant slices in a single layer on the baking sheets. Brush both sides of the eggplant slices with olive oil.
3. Bake for 20-25 minutes, or until eggplant is tender and beginning to brown, flipping halfway through.
4. In a baking dish, spread a thin layer of low-sodium tomato sauce. Layer half of the baked eggplant slices over the sauce.
5. Sprinkle half of the mozzarella and Parmesan cheeses over the eggplant. Season with half of the oregano, basil, and black pepper. Repeat the layers with the remaining ingredients.
6. Bake in the preheated oven for 20 minutes, or until the cheese is melted and bubbly.
7. Garnish with fresh basil leaves before serving.

Nutritional Information:

Per serving: 220 calories, 12g protein, 20g carbohydrates, 12g fat, 6g fiber, 20mg cholesterol, 180mg sodium, 450mg potassium, 200mg phosphorus.

15. Savory Beef Stew

Yield: 4 servings | Prep time: 20 minutes |
Cook time: 2 hours

Ingredients:

- 1 pound beef stew meat, trimmed of fat and cubed
- 2 tablespoons olive oil
- 4 cups low-sodium beef broth
- 1 onion, chopped
- 2 carrots, peeled and sliced
- 2 stalks celery, sliced
- 1 teaspoon dried thyme
- 1 teaspoon dried rosemary
- 2 bay leaves
- 2 tablespoons cornstarch mixed with 2 tablespoons water (as a thickener)
- Freshly ground black pepper to taste
- Chopped fresh parsley for garnish

Directions:

1. In a large pot, heat 1 tablespoon of olive oil over medium-high heat. Add the beef cubes and sear on all sides until browned. Remove the beef and set aside.
2. In the same pot, add the remaining olive oil, onion, carrots, and celery. Sauté until the vegetables are softened, about 5 minutes.
3. Return the beef to the pot. Add the low-sodium beef broth, thyme, rosemary, and bay leaves. Bring to a boil, then reduce heat to low, cover, and simmer for 1.5 hours, or until the beef is tender.
4. Remove the bay leaves. Stir the cornstarch mixture into the stew to thicken the broth. Simmer for an additional 10 minutes, stirring occasionally.
5. Season with freshly ground black pepper to taste. Garnish with chopped parsley before serving.

Nutritional Information:

Per serving: 300 calories, 25g protein, 15g carbohydrates, 15g fat, 3g fiber, 70mg cholesterol, 150mg sodium, 500mg potassium, 200mg phosphorus.

16. Quinoa Stuffed Peppers

Yield: 4 servings | Prep time: 15 minutes |
Cook time: 35 minutes

Ingredients:

- 4 large bell peppers, halved and seeds removed
- 1 cup quinoa, rinsed
- 2 cups low-sodium vegetable broth
- 1 tablespoon olive oil
- 1 small onion, diced
- 1 clove garlic, minced
- 1 cup diced zucchini 1 cup diced tomatoes
- 1/2 cup corn kernels (fresh or frozen)
- 1 teaspoon: dried oregano , dried basil.
- 1 cup shredded mozzarella cheese
- Freshly ground black pepper to taste

Directions:

1. Preheat the oven to 375°F (190°C). Arrange the bell pepper halves in a baking dish, cut-side up.
2. In a saucepan, bring the low-sodium vegetable broth to a boil. Add the quinoa, reduce heat to low, cover, and simmer for 15 minutes, or until the liquid is absorbed. Fluff with a fork.
3. Heat the olive oil in a skillet over medium heat. Add the onion and garlic, and sauté until softened, about 5 minutes. Add the zucchini, tomatoes, and corn, and cook for another 5 minutes. Stir in the cooked quinoa, oregano, and basil. Season with black pepper.
4. Spoon the quinoa and vegetable mixture into the bell pepper halves. Top each with shredded low-sodium mozzarella cheese.
5. Cover the baking dish with foil and bake for 20 minutes. Remove the foil and bake for an additional 15 minutes, or until the peppers are tender and the cheese is bubbly and golden.
6. Serve warm, garnished with fresh herbs if desired.

Nutritional Information:

Per serving: 300 calories, 12g protein, 40g carbohydrates, 10g fat, 6g fiber, 20mg cholesterol, 150mg sodium, 500mg potassium, 200mg phosphorus.

17. Kidney-Friendly Vegetarian Chili

Yield: 4 servings | Prep time: 15 minutes | Cook time: 30 minutes

Ingredients:

- 1 tablespoon olive oil
- 1 medium onion, diced
- 2 cloves garlic, minced
- 1 bell pepper, diced
- 1 zucchini, diced
- 2 cups low-potassium canned beans (e.g., chickpeas or lentils), rinsed and drained
- 2 cups low-sodium tomato sauce
- 1 cup water or low-sodium vegetable broth
- 1 teaspoon ground cumin
- 1 teaspoon paprika
- 1/2 teaspoon chili powder (adjust to taste)
- 1/2 teaspoon dried oregano
- Freshly ground black pepper to taste
- Fresh cilantro, chopped, for garnish

Directions:

1. Heat olive oil in a large pot over medium heat. Add the onion and garlic, sautéing until soft and fragrant, about 5 minutes.
2. Add the bell pepper and zucchini to the pot. Cook, stirring occasionally, until the vegetables are slightly softened, about 5 minutes.
3. Stir in the rinsed beans, low-sodium tomato sauce, water or vegetable broth, cumin, paprika, chili powder, oregano, and black pepper. Bring the mixture to a simmer.
4. Reduce heat to low and let the chili simmer, uncovered, for about 20 minutes, or until the vegetables are tender and the chili has thickened.
5. Adjust seasonings to taste. Serve hot, garnished with fresh cilantro.

Nutritional Information:

Per serving: 200 calories, 10g protein, 35g carbohydrates, 5g fat, 10g fiber, 0mg cholesterol, 200mg sodium, 400mg potassium, 150mg phosphorus.

18. Whole Wheat Pasta Primavera

Yield: 4 servings | Prep time: 15 minutes | Cook time: 20.minutes

Ingredients:

- 8 ounces whole wheat pasta
- 2 tablespoons olive oil
- 1 cup broccoli florets
- 1 cup sliced bell peppers (any color)
- 1 cup sliced zucchini
- 1/2 cup cherry tomatoes, halved
- 2 cloves garlic, minced
- Freshly ground black pepper to taste
- Fresh basil leaves, for garnish
- Grated Parmesan cheese (optional, check for low sodium)

Directions:

1. Cook the whole wheat pasta according to package instructions until al dente. Drain and set aside, reserving a cup of pasta water.
2. While the pasta is cooking, steam the broccoli, bell peppers, and zucchini until they are tender-crisp, about 5 minutes. Avoid overcooking to maintain low potassium levels.
3. Heat the olive oil in a large skillet over medium heat. Add the minced garlic and sauté for 1 minute until fragrant.
4. Add the steamed vegetables and cherry tomatoes to the skillet. Cook for an additional 2 minutes, stirring frequently.
5. Toss the cooked pasta with the vegetable mixture in the skillet. If the mixture seems dry, add a little of the reserved pasta water until you reach the desired consistency.
6. Season with freshly ground black pepper and garnish with fresh basil leaves. Serve with grated Parmesan cheese if desired.

Nutritional Information:

Per serving: 280 calories, 10g protein, 48g carbohydrates, 7g fat, 8g fiber, 0mg cholesterol, 30mg sodium, 400mg potassium, 150mg phosphorus.

19. Roasted Vegetable Ratatouille

Yield: 4 servings | Prep time: 20 minutes | Cook time: 40 minutes

Ingredients:

- 1 medium zucchini, sliced into rounds
- 1 medium yellow squash, sliced into rounds
- 1 medium eggplant, sliced into rounds
- 1 bell pepper (any color), sliced
- 2 medium tomatoes, sliced
- 1 onion, sliced
- 3 cloves garlic, minced
- 2 tablespoons olive oil
- 1 teaspoon dried thyme
- 1 teaspoon dried oregano
- Freshly ground black pepper to taste
- Fresh basil for garnish

Directions:

1. Preheat the oven to 375°F (190°C). Line a large baking sheet with parchment paper.
2. In a large bowl, toss the zucchini, yellow squash, eggplant, bell pepper, tomatoes, and onion with olive oil, minced garlic, thyme, oregano, and black pepper until everything is evenly coated.
3. Arrange the vegetables in a single layer on the prepared baking sheet. Try to keep the slices of zucchini, yellow squash, and eggplant separate from each other to ensure even cooking.
4. Roast in the preheated oven for about 40 minutes, or until the vegetables are tender and lightly browned at the edges.
5. Remove from the oven and let cool slightly. Transfer the roasted vegetables to a serving dish, layering them if desired, and garnish with fresh basil leaves.

Nutritional Information:

Per serving: 150 calories, 4g protein, 20g carbohydrates, 7g fat, 9g fiber, 0mg cholesterol, 30mg sodium, 500mg potassium, 100mg phosphorus.

20. Maple-Glazed Pork Chops

Yield: 4 servings | Prep time: 10 minutes | Cook time: 20 minutes

Ingredients:

- 4 pork chops, bone-in or boneless (about 6 ounces each)
- 2 tablespoons olive oil
- 1/4 cup sugar-free maple syrup
- 1 tablespoon Dijon mustard (check for low sodium)
- 1 clove garlic, minced
- 1 teaspoon apple cider vinegar
- Freshly ground black pepper to taste
- Fresh thyme or rosemary for garnish

Directions:

1. Preheat your grill or skillet over medium-high heat.
2. In a small bowl, whisk together the sugar-free maple syrup, Dijon mustard, minced garlic, and apple cider vinegar to create the glaze.
3. Season the pork chops with freshly ground black pepper. Brush one side of the pork chops with the maple glaze.
4. Place the pork chops, glazed side down, on the grill or skillet. Grill for about 5-7 minutes on one side. While cooking, brush the top side with more glaze.
5. Flip the pork chops and cook for another 5-7 minutes, or until the internal temperature reaches 145°F (63°C) and they are nicely glazed and slightly charred.
6. Let the pork chops rest for a few minutes before serving.
7. Garnish with fresh thyme or rosemary.

Nutritional Information:

Per serving: 250 calories, 25g protein, 5g carbohydrates, 14g fat, 0g fiber, 75mg cholesterol, 120mg sodium, 400mg potassium, 250mg phosphorus.

21. Cod with Parsley Pesto

Yield: 4 servings | Prep time: 15 minutes | Cook time: 15 minutes

Ingredients:

- 4 cod fillets (about 6 ounces each)
- 2 tablespoons olive oil
- Salt substitute (potassium-free) and freshly ground black pepper to taste
- For the Parsley Pesto:
- 1 cup fresh parsley leaves
- 1/4 cup grated Parmesan cheese (low-sodium)
- 2 cloves garlic
- 1/4 cup olive oil
- Salt substitute (potassium-free) and freshly ground black pepper to taste

Directions:

1. Preheat the oven to 400°F (200°C). Line a baking sheet with parchment paper.
2. Place the cod fillets on the prepared baking sheet. Brush each fillet with olive oil and season with salt substitute and black pepper.
3. Bake the cod in the preheated oven for about 12-15 minutes, or until the fish flakes easily with a fork.
4. While the cod is baking, make the parsley pesto. In a food processor, combine the parsley leaves, grated Parmesan, garlic, and a pinch of salt substitute and black pepper. Pulse until the ingredients are coarsely chopped. With the processor running, gradually add 1/4 cup olive oil until the pesto reaches your desired consistency.
5. Once the cod is cooked, remove from the oven and let it rest for a few minutes.
6. Serve the baked cod topped with a spoonful of the homemade parsley pesto.

Nutritional Information:

Per serving: 280 calories, 28g protein, 2g carbohydrates, 18g fat, 0g fiber, 65mg cholesterol, 120mg sodium, 500mg potassium, 250mg phosphorus.

22. Herb-Grilled Chicken with Quinoa Salad

Yield: 4 servings | Prep time: 20 minutes | Cook time: 30 minutes

Ingredients:

- 4 lean chicken breasts (about 6 ounces each)
- 1 tablespoon olive oil
- 2 cloves garlic, minced
- 1 teaspoon dried rosemary
- 1 teaspoon dried thyme
- 1 teaspoon dried oregano
- 2 cups cooked quinoa (cooked in low-sodium chicken or vegetable broth)
- 1 cup diced cucumbers
- 1 cup cherry tomatoes, halved
- 1/4 cup diced red onion
- 2 tablespoons lemon juice
- 2 tablespoons extra virgin olive oil
- Salt substitute (potassium-free) and pepper to taste
- Fresh parsley, chopped, for garnish

Directions:

1. In a small bowl, mix 1 tablespoon olive oil, minced garlic, rosemary, thyme, oregano, and a pinch of pepper. Rub this mixture over the chicken breasts and let marinate for at least 15 minutes.
2. Preheat the grill to medium-high heat. Grill the chicken breasts for about 6-7 minutes on each side, or until the internal temperature reaches 165°F (74°C). Remove from grill and let rest.
3. In a large bowl, combine the cooked quinoa, diced cucumbers, cherry tomatoes, red onion, lemon juice, and extra virgin olive oil. Season with a salt substitute and pepper to taste. Toss gently.
4. Slice the rested chicken breasts and serve on top of the quinoa salad. Garnish with fresh parsley.

Nutritional Information:

Per serving: 350 calories, 30g protein, 30g carbohydrates, 10g fat, 5g fiber, 75mg cholesterol, 150mg sodium, 400mg potassium, 200mg phosphorus.

1. Crispy Garlic Toasts

Yield: 4 servings | Prep time: 5 minutes | Cook time: 10 minutes

Ingredients:

- 4 slices of whole grain bread
- 2 tablespoons olive oil
- 1 teaspoon garlic powder
- Freshly ground black pepper to taste
- Fresh parsley, chopped (for garnish, optional)

Directions:

1. Preheat your oven to 375°F (190°C). Line a baking sheet with parchment paper.
2. Brush both sides of each whole grain bread slice with olive oil. Sprinkle garlic powder and freshly ground black pepper evenly over one side of each slice.
3. Place the bread slices on the prepared baking sheet. Bake in the preheated oven for about 5 minutes, then flip each slice and bake for another 5 minutes, or until the bread is crispy and golden brown around the edges.
4. Remove the toasts from the oven and let them cool slightly on a wire rack for crispiness.
5. Garnish with chopped fresh parsley before serving, if desired.

Nutritional Information:

Per serving: 150 calories, 4g protein, 18g carbohydrates, 7g fat, 3g fiber, 0mg cholesterol, 150mg sodium, 100mg potassium, 75mg phosphorus.

2. Zesty Lemon Hummus

Yield: 4 servings | Prep time: 10 minutes | Cook time: 0 minutes

Ingredients:

- 1 can (15 ounces) chickpeas, rinsed and drained
- 1/4 cup low-sodium tahini
- 1/4 cup lemon juice
- 2 cloves garlic, minced
- 2 tablespoons olive oil
- 1/2 teaspoon ground cumin
- Freshly ground black pepper to taste
- 2 tablespoons water (adjust for desired consistency)
- Fresh parsley, chopped (for garnish)

Directions:

1. In a food processor, combine the chickpeas, low-sodium tahini, lemon juice, minced garlic, olive oil, ground cumin, and a pinch of freshly ground black pepper. Blend until smooth.
2. While blending, gradually add water until you reach your desired consistency. The hummus should be creamy and smooth.
3. Taste and adjust the seasoning if necessary, adding more lemon juice or pepper as needed.
4. Transfer the hummus to a serving bowl. Drizzle with a little olive oil and garnish with chopped fresh parsley before serving.
5. Serve with vegetable sticks, whole grain crackers, or as a spread on sandwiches.

Nutritional Information:

Per serving: 200 calories, 6g protein, 20g carbohydrates, 12g fat, 5g fiber, 0mg cholesterol, 150mg sodium, 250mg potassium, 150mg phosphorus.

3. Cucumber Dill Bites4. Herbed Greek Yogurt Dip

Yield: 4 servings | Prep time: 10 minutes | Cook time: 0 minutes

Ingredients:

- 2 large cucumbers, sliced into 1/2-inch thick rounds
- 4 ounces cream cheese, softened (look for low-sodium options)
- 1 tablespoon fresh dill, chopped
- 1/2 teaspoon garlic powder
- Freshly ground black pepper to taste

Directions:

1. In a small bowl, mix together the softened cream cheese, chopped fresh dill, garlic powder, and a pinch of black pepper until well combined.
2. Arrange the cucumber slices on a serving platter.
3. Using a small spoon or a piping bag, top each cucumber slice with a dollop of the dill cream cheese mixture.
4. Optionally, garnish each bite with a tiny sprig of dill or a sprinkle of black pepper for added visual appeal.
5. Chill in the refrigerator for about 10 minutes before serving to allow the flavors to meld.

Nutritional Information:

Per serving: 100 calories, 2g protein, 4g carbohydrates, 8g fat, 1g fiber, 20mg cholesterol, 80mg sodium, 200mg potassium, 50mg phosphorus.

4. Herbed Greek Yogurt Dip

Yield: 4 servings | Prep time: 10 minutes | Cook time: 0 minutes

Ingredients:

- 1 cup low-fat Greek yogurt
- 1 tablespoon fresh dill, finely chopped
- 1 tablespoon fresh chives, finely chopped
- 1 clove garlic, minced
- 1 teaspoon lemon zest
- 1 tablespoon lemon juice
- Freshly ground black pepper to taste
- Vegetable sticks (carrots, bell peppers, cucumbers) for serving

Directions:

1. In a mixing bowl, combine the Greek yogurt, chopped dill, chives, minced garlic, lemon zest, and lemon juice. Stir until all the ingredients are well incorporated.
2. Season the dip with freshly ground black pepper to taste. Mix thoroughly.
3. Chill the dip in the refrigerator for at least 30 minutes to allow the flavors to meld together.
4. Serve the herbed Greek yogurt dip with a variety of vegetable sticks such as carrots, bell peppers, and cucumbers.

Nutritional Information:

Per serving: 60 calories, 9g protein, 5g carbohydrates, 0.5g fat, 0g fiber, 5mg cholesterol, 45mg sodium, 150mg potassium, 100mg phosphorus.

5. Savory Baked Apple Chips

Yield: 4 servings | Prep time: 10 minutes |
Cook time: 2 hours

Ingredients:

- 2 large apples, any variety
- 1/2 teaspoon ground cinnamon
- Cooking spray or a brush of olive oil (for the baking sheet)

Directions:

1. Preheat your oven to 200°F (93°C). Prepare a baking sheet by lightly coating it with cooking spray or brushing it with olive oil.
2. Core the apples and slice them very thinly, approximately 1/8 inch thick, using a mandoline slicer or a sharp knife.
3. Arrange the apple slices in a single layer on the prepared baking sheet. Make sure the slices do not overlap to ensure even baking.
4. Sprinkle the ground cinnamon evenly over the apple slices.
5. Bake in the preheated oven for 1 hour. After 1 hour, flip the apple slices and continue baking for another hour, or until the apple chips are crisp and no longer moist.
6. Remove the apple chips from the oven and let them cool completely on a wire rack. They will continue to crisp up as they cool.
7. Serve the savory baked apple chips as a snack or side.

Nutritional Information:

Per serving: 50 calories, 0g protein,
13g carbohydrates, 0g fat, 2g fiber,
0mg cholesterol, 0mg sodium,
100mg potassium, 20mg phosphorus.

6. Mini Rice Cakes with Avocado and Tomato Salsa

Yield: 4 servings | Prep time: 15 minutes |
Cook time: 0 minutes

Ingredients:

- 12 mini rice cakes
- 1 ripe avocado, peeled and mashed
- 1/2 cup cherry tomatoes, finely chopped
- 1/4 cup red onion, finely chopped
- 1 tablespoon lime juice
- 1 tablespoon cilantro, chopped (optional)
- Freshly ground black pepper to taste

Directions:

1. In a small bowl, combine the mashed avocado, chopped cherry tomatoes, red onion, lime juice, and cilantro (if using). Season with freshly ground black pepper to taste and mix well to combine.
2. Place the mini rice cakes on a serving platter.
3. Top each mini rice cake with a spoonful of the avocado and tomato salsa.
4. Serve immediately, or refrigerate the salsa if preparing in advance and top the rice cakes just before serving to maintain their crispness.

Nutritional Information:

Per serving: 100 calories, 2g protein,
15g carbohydrates, 5g fat, 3g fiber,
0mg cholesterol, 30mg sodium,
200mg potassium, 50mg phosphorus.

7. Cheesy Cauliflower Popcorn

Yield: 4 servings | Prep time: 10 minutes | Cook time: 25 minutes

Ingredients:

- 1 large head of cauliflower, cut into small florets
- 2 tablespoons olive oil
- 1/4 cup nutritional yeast
- 1/2 teaspoon garlic powder
- Freshly ground black pepper to taste

Directions:

1. Preheat your oven to 425°F (220°C). Line a baking sheet with parchment paper.
2. In a large bowl, toss the cauliflower florets with olive oil, ensuring each piece is well coated.
3. Add the nutritional yeast and garlic powder to the bowl. Toss again until the cauliflower is evenly coated with the nutritional yeast and spices.
4. Spread the cauliflower florets in a single layer on the prepared baking sheet. Season with freshly ground black pepper.
5. Roast in the preheated oven for about 20-25 minutes, or until the cauliflower is golden brown and crispy, stirring halfway through the cooking time.
6. Serve the cheesy cauliflower popcorn immediately as a snack or side dish.

Nutritional Information:

Per serving: 120 calories, 6g protein, 10g carbohydrates, 7g fat, 4g fiber, 0mg cholesterol, 30mg sodium, 300mg potassium, 100mg phosphorus.

8. Tangy Tzatziki Sauce

Yield: 4 servings | Prep time: 15 minutes | Cook time: 0 minutes

Ingredients:

- 1 cup low-fat Greek yogurt
- 1 medium cucumber, seeded and finely grated
- 2 cloves garlic, minced
- 1 tablespoon fresh lemon juice
- 1 tablespoon fresh dill, chopped (or 1 teaspoon dried dill)
- Salt substitute (potassium-free) and freshly ground black pepper to taste

Directions:

1. Place the grated cucumber in a fine mesh sieve or on a clean kitchen towel and squeeze to remove excess moisture.
2. In a medium bowl, combine the drained cucumber, low-fat Greek yogurt, minced garlic, lemon juice, and chopped dill. Stir until well mixed.
3. Season with a salt substitute and freshly ground black pepper to taste. Mix again to evenly distribute the seasonings.
4. Cover and refrigerate for at least 1 hour to allow the flavors to meld.
5. Serve the tzatziki sauce chilled with an assortment of raw vegetables such as carrot sticks, bell pepper slices, and cherry tomatoes.

Nutritional Information:

Per serving: 45 calories, 6g protein, 5g carbohydrates, 0.5g fat, 0.5g fiber, 5mg cholesterol, 30mg sodium, 150mg potassium, 100mg phosphorus.

9. Oven-Roasted Chickpeas

Yield: 4 servings | Prep time: 10 minutes | Cook time: 40 minutes

Ingredients:

- 1 can (15 ounces) chickpeas, rinsed and drained
- 1 tablespoon olive oil
- 1/2 teaspoon paprika
- Salt substitute (potassium-free) to taste
- Freshly ground black pepper to taste

Directions:

1. Preheat your oven to 400°F (200°C). Line a baking sheet with parchment paper.
2. Dry the chickpeas thoroughly with a kitchen towel or paper towels. Removing as much moisture as possible will help them roast to a crisp texture.
3. In a bowl, toss the dried chickpeas with olive oil, paprika, a pinch of salt substitute, and black pepper until evenly coated.
4. Spread the chickpeas in a single layer on the prepared baking sheet.
5. Roast in the preheated oven for about 35-40 minutes, stirring every 10 minutes, until golden brown and crispy.
6. Remove from the oven and let cool slightly. They will continue to crisp up as they cool.
7. Serve the oven-roasted chickpeas as a snack or a crunchy salad topping.

Nutritional Information:

Per serving: 130 calories, 5g protein, 18g carbohydrates, 5g fat, 5g fiber, 0mg cholesterol, 50mg sodium, 200mg potassium, 100mg phosphorus.

10. Kale Chips with Sea Salt

Yield: 4 servings | Prep time: 10 minutes | Cook time: 15 minutes

Ingredients:

- 1 large bunch of kale, washed and dried
- 1 tablespoon olive oil
- 1/4 teaspoon sea salt

Directions:

1. Preheat your oven to 350°F (175°C). Line a baking sheet with parchment paper.
2. Remove the kale leaves from their stems and tear them into bite-sized pieces.
3. In a large bowl, toss the kale pieces with olive oil, ensuring each piece is lightly coated.
4. Arrange the kale pieces in a single layer on the prepared baking sheet, avoiding overlap to ensure even baking.
5. Sprinkle the sea salt evenly over the kale.
6. Bake in the preheated oven for about 10-15 minutes, or until the edges are slightly browned and the kale is crispy.
7. Remove from the oven and let the kale chips cool for a few minutes before serving. They will continue to crisp up as they cool.

Nutritional Information:

Per serving: 60 calories, 2g protein, 7g carbohydrates, 3g fat, 2g fiber, 0mg cholesterol, 150mg sodium, 300mg potassium, 50mg phosphorus.

11. Stuffed Mini Bell Peppers

Yield: 4 servings | Prep time: 15 minutes | Cook time: 20 minutes

Ingredients:

- 12 mini bell peppers, halved and seeded
- 1 cup cooked rice (preferably brown rice for added fiber)
- 2 tablespoons olive oil
- 1/4 cup onion, finely chopped
- 1 clove garlic, minced
- 1/4 cup fresh parsley, chopped
- 1 tablespoon fresh basil, chopped
- Salt substitute (potassium-free) and freshly ground black pepper to taste

Directions:

1. Preheat the oven to 375°F (190°C). Line a baking sheet with parchment paper.
2. In a skillet over medium heat, warm 1 tablespoon olive oil. Add the onion and garlic, sautéing until soft, about 3-5 minutes.
3. In a large bowl, combine the sautéed onion and garlic with the cooked rice, parsley, and basil. Season with a salt substitute and black pepper to taste.
4. Stuff each mini bell pepper half with the rice mixture, pressing gently to fill them up.
5. Place the stuffed peppers on the prepared baking sheet. Drizzle with the remaining olive oil.
6. Bake in the preheated oven for about 15-20 minutes, or until the peppers are tender and the filling is heated through.
7. Serve warm as a flavorful and colorful side dish.

Nutritional Information:

Per serving: 150 calories, 3g protein, 20g carbohydrates, 7g fat, 3g fiber, 0mg cholesterol, 50mg sodium, 250mg potassium, 100mg phosphorus.

12. Eggplant Bruschetta

Yield: 4 servings | Prep time: 15 minutes | Cook time: 10 minutes

Ingredients:

- 1 large eggplant, sliced into 1/2-inch rounds
- 2 tablespoons olive oil
- 2 medium tomatoes, finely chopped
- 1/4 cup fresh basil leaves, chopped
- 1 clove garlic, minced
- Salt substitute (potassium-free) and freshly ground black pepper to taste
- Balsamic vinegar reduction (optional, for drizzling)

Directions:

1. Preheat a grill or grill pan over medium-high heat.
2. Brush both sides of each eggplant slice with olive oil.
3. Grill the eggplant slices for about 4-5 minutes on each side, or until they are tender and have grill marks.
4. In a small bowl, combine the chopped tomatoes, basil, and minced garlic. Season with a salt substitute and black pepper to taste.
5. Top each grilled eggplant slice with a spoonful of the tomato and basil mixture.
6. Optionally, drizzle with balsamic vinegar reduction for added flavor.
7. Serve immediately as a flavorful and healthy appetizer.

Nutritional Information:

Per serving: 90 calories, 2g protein, 10g carbohydrates, 5g fat, 4g fiber, 0mg cholesterol, 30mg sodium, 300mg potassium, 60mg phosphorus.

13. Carrot and Zucchini Fritters

Yield: 4 servings | Prep time: 20 minutes | Cook time: 10 minutes

Ingredients:

- 2 medium zucchinis, shredded
- 2 medium carrots, shredded
- 1/4 cup all-purpose flour (or a kidney-friendly flour alternative)
- 1 egg, lightly beaten
- 1/2 teaspoon garlic powder
- Salt substitute (potassium-free) and freshly ground black pepper to taste
- 2 tablespoons olive oil for frying

Directions:

1. Place the shredded zucchini in a colander, sprinkle with a little salt substitute, and let sit for 10 minutes to draw out moisture. Squeeze out the excess water.
2. In a large bowl, mix the drained zucchini, shredded carrots, flour, beaten egg, garlic powder, and a pinch of salt substitute and pepper until well combined.
3. Heat the olive oil in a large skillet over medium heat.
4. Form the vegetable mixture into small patties, about 2 inches in diameter, and flatten slightly.
5. Fry the patties in batches, cooking for about 3-4 minutes on each side or until golden brown and crispy.
6. Transfer the fritters to a paper towel-lined plate to drain any excess oil.
7. Serve warm as a snack or a side dish.

Nutritional Information:

Per serving: 150 calories, 4g protein, 15g carbohydrates, 9g fat, 3g fiber, 47mg cholesterol, 75mg sodium, 200mg potassium, 100mg phosphorus.

14. Sweet Potato Wedges

Yield: 4 servings | Prep time: 10 minutes | Cook time: 25 minutes

Ingredients:

- 2 large sweet potatoes, washed and cut into wedges
- 2 tablespoons olive oil
- 1 teaspoon dried rosemary (or herb of choice)
- Salt substitute (potassium-free) to taste
- Freshly ground black pepper to taste

Directions:

1. Preheat your oven to 425°F (220°C). Line a baking sheet with parchment paper.
2. In a large bowl, toss the sweet potato wedges with olive oil, dried rosemary, a pinch of salt substitute, and black pepper until well coated.
3. Spread the sweet potato wedges in a single layer on the prepared baking sheet, making sure not to overcrowd them for even cooking.
4. Bake in the preheated oven for about 20-25 minutes, or until the wedges are golden brown and crispy on the edges. Flip halfway through baking to ensure even crispiness.
5. Remove from the oven and let cool for a few minutes before serving.

Nutritional Information:

Per serving: 200 calories, 2g protein, 30g carbohydrates, 7g fat, 5g fiber, 0mg cholesterol, 30mg sodium, 400mg potassium, 60mg phosphorus.

15. Chilled Cucumber Soup

Yield: 4 servings | Prep time: 15 minutes |
Cook time: 0 minutes (chill time: at least 2 hours)

Ingredients:

- 4 large cucumbers, peeled and roughly chopped
- 2 cups low-fat Greek yogurt
- 2 tablespoons fresh dill, chopped
- 2 cloves garlic, minced
- 1 tablespoon lemon juice
- Salt substitute (potassium-free) and freshly ground black pepper to taste
- 1 tablespoon olive oil (for garnish)
- Fresh dill sprigs (for garnish)

Directions:

1. In a blender, combine cucumbers, low-fat Greek yogurt, chopped dill, minced garlic, and lemon juice. Blend until smooth.
2. Season the soup with a salt substitute and freshly ground black pepper to taste. Blend again to incorporate the seasonings.
3. Transfer the soup to a large bowl. Cover and refrigerate for at least 2 hours, allowing the flavors to meld and the soup to chill thoroughly.
4. Before serving, stir the soup well. Adjust seasoning if necessary.
5. Serve the chilled soup in individual bowls, drizzled with a bit of olive oil and garnished with fresh dill sprigs.

Nutritional Information:

Per serving: 120 calories, 8g protein,
15g carbohydrates, 4g fat, 2g fiber,
10mg cholesterol, 50mg sodium,
400mg potassium, 150mg phosphorus.

16. Parmesan Zucchini Rounds

Yield: 4 servings | Prep time: 10 minutes |
Cook time: 15 minutes

Ingredients:

- 2 large zucchinis, sliced into 1/4-inch rounds
- 1/2 cup grated Parmesan cheese
- Salt substitute (potassium-free) and freshly ground black pepper to taste
- Olive oil spray (or 1 tablespoon olive oil)

Directions:

1. Preheat your oven to 425°F (220°C). Line a baking sheet with parchment paper or lightly grease it.
2. Arrange zucchini rounds in a single layer on the baking sheet. Lightly spray with olive oil or brush each round with olive oil.
3. Season with a salt substitute and freshly ground black pepper.
4. Sprinkle grated Parmesan cheese evenly over the zucchini rounds.
5. Bake in the preheated oven for about 15 minutes, or until the zucchini is tender and the Parmesan is melted and slightly golden.
6. Optional: For a more golden and crispy top, broil for an additional 1-2 minutes, watching carefully to avoid burning.
7. Serve warm as a side dish.

Nutritional Information:

Per serving: 80 calories, 5g protein,
4g carbohydrates, 5g fat, 1g fiber,
7mg cholesterol, 150mg sodium,
250mg potassium, 120mg phosphorus.

17. Ricotta and Lemon Zest Crostini

Yield: 4 servings | Prep time: 10 minutes | Cook time: 5 minutes

Ingredients:

- 1 baguette, sliced into 1/2-inch thick rounds
- 1 cup ricotta cheese
- Zest of 1 lemon
- 2 tablespoons olive oil
- Salt substitute (potassium-free) and freshly ground black pepper to taste
- Fresh herbs for garnish (optional, such as basil or thyme)

Directions:

1. Preheat your oven's broiler.
2. Arrange baguette slices on a baking sheet and brush lightly with olive oil. Broil for 1-2 minutes on each side, or until golden and crispy. Watch closely to prevent burning.
3. In a small bowl, mix ricotta cheese with half of the lemon zest, a pinch of salt substitute, and black pepper until well combined.
4. Spread a generous amount of the ricotta mixture on each toasted baguette slice.
5. Garnish each crostini with the remaining lemon zest and optional fresh herbs.
6. Serve immediately as a refreshing and flavorful appetizer.

Nutritional Information:

Per serving: 200 calories, 9g protein, 20g carbohydrates, 9g fat, 1g fiber, 31mg cholesterol, 125mg sodium, 100mg potassium, 150mg phosphorus.

18. Beetroot and Goat Cheese Salad

Yield: 4 servings | Prep time: 15 minutes | Cook time: 0 minutes (assuming pre-cooked beetroots)

Ingredients:

- 4 medium beetroots, cooked, peeled, and sliced
- 4 ounces low-sodium goat cheese, crumbled
- 4 cups mixed salad greens (such as arugula, spinach, and watercress)
- 2 tablespoons olive oil
- 1 tablespoon balsamic vinegar
- Salt substitute (potassium-free) and freshly ground black pepper to taste
- 1/4 cup walnuts, toasted and chopped (optional)

Directions:

1. Arrange the mixed salad greens on a large serving platter or divide among individual plates.
2. Top the greens with sliced beetroots, distributing them evenly.
3. Sprinkle crumbled low-sodium goat cheese over the beetroots.
4. In a small bowl, whisk together olive oil and balsamic vinegar with a pinch of salt substitute and black pepper. Drizzle this dressing over the salad.
5. Garnish with toasted walnuts if using for added texture and flavor.
6. Serve immediately, offering a combination of earthy beetroots, creamy goat cheese, and crisp greens.

Nutritional Information:

Per serving: 200 calories, 7g protein, 13g carbohydrates, 14g fat, 3g fiber, 13mg cholesterol, 100mg sodium, 400mg potassium, 150mg phosphorus.

19. Roasted Asparagus Spears

Yield: 4 servings | Prep time: 5 minutes |
Cook time: 15 minutes

Ingredients:

- 1 lb (about 450g) fresh asparagus, ends trimmed
- 2 tablespoons olive oil
- Juice of 1 lemon
- Salt substitute (potassium-free) and freshly ground black pepper to taste

Directions:

1. Preheat your oven to 400°F (200°C). Line a baking sheet with parchment paper.
2. Place the asparagus on the prepared baking sheet and drizzle with olive oil. Toss gently to coat.
3. Squeeze lemon juice evenly over the asparagus. Season with a salt substitute and black pepper to taste.
4. Roast in the preheated oven for about 12-15 minutes, or until the asparagus is tender and lightly browned at the edges.
5. Serve immediately, offering a vibrant and healthy side that pairs well with a variety of main dishes.

Nutritional Information:

Per serving: 90 calories, 3g protein,
6g carbohydrates, 7g fat, 3g fiber,
0mg cholesterol, 30mg sodium,
230mg potassium, 50mg phosphorus.

20. Sesame Green Beans

Yield: 4 servings | Prep time: 10 minutes |
Cook time: 10 minutes

Ingredients:

- 1 lb (about 450g) fresh green beans, trimmed
- 1 tablespoon sesame oil
- 2 tablespoons sesame seeds
- Salt substitute (potassium-free) to taste
- Freshly ground black pepper to taste

Directions:

1. Blanch the green beans in boiling water for 2-3 minutes until they are bright green but still crisp. Drain and immediately rinse under cold water to stop the cooking process.
2. In a large skillet, heat the sesame oil over medium heat. Add the blanched green beans and toss to coat.
3. Cook for 5-7 minutes, stirring occasionally, until the beans are tender but still slightly crisp.
4. Sprinkle sesame seeds over the green beans and toss well. Cook for an additional 2 minutes, allowing the sesame seeds to lightly toast and become fragrant.
5. Season with a salt substitute and black pepper to taste.
6. Serve warm as a flavorful and nutritious side dish.

Nutritional Information:

Per serving: 100 calories, 3g protein,
8g carbohydrates, 7g fat, 4g fiber,
0mg cholesterol, 30mg sodium,
230mg potassium, 70mg phosphorus.

21. Vegetable Spring Rolls

Yield: 4 servings | Prep time: 20 minutes | Cook time: 0 minutes

Ingredients:

- 8 rice paper wrappers
- 1 cup lettuce, shredded
- 1 carrot, julienned
- 1 cucumber, julienned
- 1 bell pepper, julienned
- 1/4 cup fresh cilantro leaves
- 1/4 cup fresh mint leaves
- For the Peanut Dipping Sauce:
- 2 tablespoons peanut butter (unsalted, if available)
- 1 tablespoon low-sodium soy sauce
- 1 tablespoon lime juice
- 1 teaspoon honey
- 2-3 tablespoons water (to thin)
- Optional: 1/4 teaspoon chili flakes for heat

Directions:

1. Fill a large bowl with warm water. Dip one rice paper wrapper into the water for about 15-20 seconds until just pliable. Lay wrapper flat on a clean work surface.
2. On the bottom third of the wrapper, place a small handful of lettuce, some carrot, cucumber, bell pepper, a few cilantro leaves, and mint leaves.
3. Roll the wrapper over the fillings, then fold in the sides and continue rolling tightly until sealed. Repeat with the remaining wrappers and filling.
4. For the peanut dipping sauce, whisk together peanut butter, low-sodium soy sauce, lime juice, honey, and water until smooth. Add chili flakes if using.
5. Serve the vegetable spring rolls immediately with the peanut dipping sauce on the side.

Nutritional Information:

Per serving: 150 calories, 4g protein, 25g carbohydrates, 4g fat, 2g fiber, 0mg cholesterol, 200mg sodium, 200mg potassium, 100mg phosphorus.

22. Mushroom Pâté

Yield: 4 servings | Prep time: 15 minutes | Cook time: 10 minutes

Ingredients:

- 1 lb (about 450g) mixed mushrooms, cleaned and chopped
- 2 tablespoons olive oil
- 1 small onion, finely chopped
- 2 cloves garlic, minced
- 1 tablespoon fresh thyme leaves
- 2 tablespoons low-sodium soy sauce or tamari
- 1/4 cup unsalted cashews (optional, for creaminess)
- Salt substitute (potassium-free) and freshly ground black pepper to taste

Directions:

1. In a large skillet, heat the olive oil over medium heat. Add the onion and garlic, sautéing until soft and translucent, about 3 minutes.
2. Increase the heat to medium-high, add the mushrooms and thyme, and cook until the mushrooms have released their moisture and started to brown, about 5-7 minutes.
3. Stir in the low-sodium soy sauce or tamari, and cook for an additional 2 minutes. Remove from heat and allow to cool slightly.
4. If using, add the cashews to a food processor and pulse until finely ground. Add the sautéed mushroom mixture to the food processor.
5. Process until the mixture is smooth and well combined, scraping down the sides as necessary. Season with the salt substitute and black pepper to taste.
6. Transfer the pâté to a serving dish and chill in the refrigerator for at least 1 hour to set and develop the flavors.
7. Serve the mushroom pâté chilled, accompanied by slices of fresh cucumber, bell peppers, or whole-grain crackers.

Nutritional Information:

Per serving: 150 calories, 5g protein, 10g carbohydrates, 10g fat, 2g fiber, 0mg cholesterol, 150mg sodium, 300mg potassium, 100mg phosphorus.

23. Spinach and Cheese Stuffed Mushrooms

Yield: 4 servings | Prep time: 20 minutes | Cook time: 20 minutes

Ingredients:

- 12 large mushrooms, stems removed
- 1 tablespoon olive oil
- 1 small onion, finely chopped
- 2 cloves garlic, minced
- 2 cups fresh spinach, chopped
- 1/2 cup low-phosphorus cheese (e.g., cream cheese or ricotta), softened
- Salt substitute (potassium-free) and freshly ground black pepper to taste
- 1/4 cup grated Parmesan cheese (optional, check for phosphorus content)

Directions:

1. Preheat the oven to 375°F (190°C). Line a baking sheet with parchment paper.
2. Heat olive oil in a skillet over medium heat. Add onion and garlic, sautéing until soft, about 3-4 minutes.
3. Add spinach to the skillet and cook until wilted, about 2 minutes. Remove from heat and let cool slightly.
4. In a mixing bowl, combine the sautéed spinach mixture with the low-phosphorus cheese. Season with a salt substitute and black pepper to taste.
5. Stuff each mushroom cap with the spinach and cheese mixture, pressing firmly.
6. Place the stuffed mushrooms on the prepared baking sheet. Sprinkle with grated Parmesan cheese if using.
7. Bake in the preheated oven for 15-20 minutes, or until the mushrooms are tender and the tops are lightly golden.
8. Serve warm as a delightful appetizer or side dish.

Nutritional Information:

Per serving: 150 calories, 6g protein, 8g carbohydrates, 10g fat, 2g fiber, 20mg cholesterol, 100mg sodium, 300mg potassium, 150mg phosphorus.

24. Quinoa Salad with Veggies

Yield: 4 servings | Prep time: 15 minutes | Cook time: 20 minutes (for quinoa)

Ingredients:

- 1 cup quinoa, rinsed
- 2 cups water
- 1 cup diced cucumbers
- 1 cup cherry tomatoes, halved
- 1/2 cup diced red bell pepper
- 1/4 cup finely chopped red onion
- 1/4 cup chopped fresh parsley
- 2 tablespoons olive oil
- 1 tablespoon lemon juice
- Salt substitute (potassium-free) and freshly ground black pepper to taste

Directions:

1. In a medium saucepan, bring 2 cups of water to a boil. Add quinoa, reduce heat to low, cover, and simmer for 15-20 minutes, or until water is absorbed and quinoa is tender. Fluff with a fork and let cool.
2. In a large bowl, combine cooled quinoa, diced cucumbers, cherry tomatoes, red bell pepper, red onion, and chopped parsley.
3. In a small bowl, whisk together olive oil, lemon juice, a pinch of salt substitute, and black pepper. Pour the dressing over the quinoa mixture and toss to combine.
4. Taste and adjust seasoning as needed. Refrigerate for at least 30 minutes before serving to allow flavors to meld.
5. Serve chilled or at room temperature as a light and refreshing side dish or meal.

Nutritional Information:

Per serving: 220 calories, 6g protein, 32g carbohydrates, 8g fat, 5g fiber, 0mg cholesterol, 50mg sodium, 300mg potassium, 150mg phosphorus.

Liquid Luxuries: 16 Invigorating Smoothies and Drinks

1. Classic Berry Smoothie

Yield: 2 servings | Prep time: 5 minutes | Cook time: 0 minutes

Ingredients:

- 1/2 cup blueberries
- 1/2 cup strawberries, hulled
- 1 cup low-fat Greek yogurt
- 1 cup unsweetened almond milk

Directions:

1. Place the blueberries, strawberries, low-fat Greek yogurt, and almond milk into a blender.
2. Blend on high speed until smooth and creamy. If the smoothie is too thick, you can add a little more almond milk to reach your desired consistency.
3. Taste and adjust the sweetness if necessary, by adding a teaspoon of honey or a sugar substitute (optional and based on dietary needs).
4. Pour the smoothie into glasses and serve immediately for the freshest flavor.
5. Garnish with a few whole berries on top for presentation if desired.

Nutritional Information:

Per serving: 150 calories, 12g protein, 20g carbohydrates, 3g fat, 3g fiber, 5mg cholesterol, 80mg sodium, 250mg potassium, 100mg phosphorus.

2. Peachy Keen Smoothie

Yield: 2 servings | Prep time: 5 minutes | Cook time: 0 minutes

Ingredients:

- 1 cup sliced peaches (fresh or frozen)
- 1 cup low-fat Greek yogurt
- 1 tablespoon honey (adjust to taste)
- 1 cup ice

Directions:

1. Add the sliced peaches, low-fat Greek yogurt, honey, and ice to a blender.
2. Blend on high until smooth and creamy. If using fresh peaches and the smoothie is too thick, you can add a little water or unsweetened almond milk to achieve your desired consistency.
3. Taste the smoothie and adjust the sweetness if necessary by adding a bit more honey, keeping in mind the nutritional focus.
4. Once blended to perfection, pour the smoothie into serving glasses.
5. Serve immediately, garnished with a slice of peach or a mint leaf for an extra touch of elegance.

Nutritional Information:

Per serving: 180 calories, 15g protein, 25g carbohydrates, 1g fat, 2g fiber, 10mg cholesterol, 60mg sodium, 300mg potassium, 150mg phosphorus.

3. Apple-Ginger Zing

Yield: 2 servings | Prep time: 10 minutes |
Cook time: 0 minutes

Ingredients:

- 1 green apple, cored and sliced
- 1-inch piece of fresh ginger, peeled
- 1 cup spinach, washed
- 1/2 cucumber, sliced

Directions:

1. Prepare the ingredients by washing and slicing the green apple and cucumber. Peel the ginger and ensure the spinach is clean.
2. Add the green apple slices, fresh ginger, spinach, and cucumber slices to a blender.
3. Blend on high until the mixture is smooth. If the smoothie is too thick, you can add a small amount of water or ice to reach your desired consistency.
4. Once fully blended, taste the smoothie. If you desire a little more sweetness, you could add a teaspoon of honey or maple syrup, keeping in mind the nutritional goals.
5. Serve the smoothie immediately, garnishing with a thin slice of apple or a sprig of mint for an extra zing.

Nutritional Information:

Per serving: 80 calories, 2g protein, 18g carbohydrates, 0.5g fat, 4g fiber, 0mg cholesterol, 20mg sodium, 290mg potassium, 55mg phosphorus.

4. Tropical Coconut Water Drink

Yield: 4 servings | Prep time: 5 minutes |
Cook time: 0 minutes

Ingredients:

- 2 cups coconut water
- 1 cup pineapple juice
- Juice of 1 lime

Directions:

1. In a large pitcher, combine the coconut water, pineapple juice, and freshly squeezed lime juice.
2. Stir well to ensure all the ingredients are thoroughly mixed.
3. Taste the mixture and adjust the flavors as needed. If you prefer it sweeter, you can add a little more pineapple juice.
4. Chill the drink in the refrigerator for at least 30 minutes before serving. This allows the flavors to meld and the drink to refresh.
5. Serve the Tropical Coconut Water Drink over ice in tall glasses, garnished with a slice of lime or pineapple for an extra tropical touch.

Nutritional Information:

Per serving: 60 calories, 1g protein, 14g carbohydrates, 0g fat, 0g fiber, 0mg cholesterol, 40mg sodium, 250mg potassium, 50mg phosphorus.

5. Cucumber Mint Refresher

Yield: 4 servings | Prep time: 10 minutes | Cook time: 0 minutes

Ingredients:

- 1 large cucumber, peeled and chopped
- 1/4 cup fresh mint leaves
- Juice of 2 lemons
- 4 cups water
- Ice cubes (optional)
- Slices of cucumber and lemon for garnish (optional)

Directions:

1. In a blender, combine the chopped cucumber, fresh mint leaves, and lemon juice. Blend until smooth.
2. Strain the mixture through a fine mesh sieve into a large pitcher, pressing on the solids to extract as much liquid as possible.
3. Add the water to the cucumber-mint juice in the pitcher and stir to combine well. Taste and adjust the lemon juice if necessary, depending on your preference for tartness.
4. Refrigerate until chilled, at least 1 hour, to allow the flavors to meld.
5. Serve over ice in individual glasses, garnished with slices of cucumber and lemon if desired.

Nutritional Information:

Per serving: 15 calories, 0.5g protein, 4g carbohydrates, 0g fat, 0.5g fiber, 0mg cholesterol, 10mg sodium, 150mg potassium, 20mg phosphorus.

6. Carrot-Apple Bliss

Yield: 4 servings | Prep time: 5 minutes | Cook time: 0 minutes

Ingredients:

- 1 cup carrot juice (use a limited quantity to control potassium levels)
- 1 apple, cored and sliced
- 3 cups water
- Ice cubes (optional)

Directions:

1. In a blender, combine the carrot juice and apple slices. Blend until the apple is fully pureed and the mixture is smooth.
2. Add water to the blender and blend again briefly to mix well. This dilutes the carrot juice, helping to control the overall potassium content.
3. Taste the mixture and adjust according to preference. If you desire a sweeter drink, you could add a small amount of honey or another sweetener of choice, keeping in mind the nutritional focus.
4. Serve the Carrot-Apple Bliss over ice in tall glasses for a refreshing drink.
5. Optionally, garnish with a thin slice of apple or a sprig of mint for an extra touch of flavor and presentation.

Nutritional Information:

Per serving: 50 calories, 1g protein, 12g carbohydrates, 0g fat, 2g fiber, 0mg cholesterol, 30mg sodium, 200mg potassium, 35mg phosphorus.

7. Banana-Almond Smoothie

Yield: 2 servings | Prep time: 5 minutes |
Cook time: 0 minutes

Ingredients:

- 1/2 banana
- 2 cups almond milk
- 2 tablespoons almond butter
- 1/2 teaspoon vanilla extract

Directions:

1. Place the half banana, almond milk, almond butter, and vanilla extract into a blender.
2. Blend on high speed until the mixture is smooth and creamy. If the smoothie is too thick for your liking, you can add a bit more almond milk to reach your desired consistency.
3. Taste the smoothie, and adjust the sweetness if necessary. Depending on your preference, you might add a touch of honey or maple syrup, but remember this will alter the nutritional profile.
4. Once blended to perfection, pour the smoothie into glasses.
5. Serve immediately for the freshest taste, optionally garnished with a slice of banana or a sprinkle of almond flakes on top for a decorative touch.

Nutritional Information:

Per serving: 180 calories, 5g protein, 20g carbohydrates, 10g fat, 4g fiber, 0mg cholesterol, 150mg sodium, 250mg potassium, 100mg phosphorus.

8. Raspberry-Lemonade Fizz

Yield: 4 servings | Prep time: 10 minutes |
Cook time: 0 minutes

Ingredients:

- 1 cup fresh raspberries
- Juice of 2 lemons
- 1-2 teaspoons stevia (adjust to taste)
- 4 cups sparkling water
- Ice cubes (optional)
- Additional raspberries and lemon slices for garnish (optional)

Directions:

1. In a blender, combine the fresh raspberries, lemon juice, and stevia. Blend until smooth.
2. Strain the raspberry-lemon mixture through a fine mesh sieve into a pitcher, pressing on the solids to extract as much liquid as possible.
3. Add the sparkling water to the pitcher and stir gently to combine.
4. Taste and adjust the sweetness by adding more stevia if desired.
5. To serve, fill glasses with ice cubes, pour the raspberry-lemonade fizz over the ice, and garnish with additional raspberries and lemon slices if using.

Nutritional Information:

Per serving: 30 calories, 0g protein, 8g carbohydrates, 0g fat, 2g fiber, 0mg cholesterol, 5mg sodium, 60mg potassium, 20mg phosphorus.

9. Cranberry Spritz

Yield: 4 servings | Prep time: 5 minutes | Cook time: 0 minutes

Ingredients:

- 2 cups unsweetened cranberry juice
- Juice of 1 lime
- 2 cups sparkling water
- Ice cubes (optional)
- Lime slices and fresh cranberries for garnish (optional)

Directions:

1. In a large pitcher, combine the unsweetened cranberry juice and lime juice. Stir well to mix.
2. Just before serving, add the sparkling water to the cranberry and lime mixture. Gently stir to combine.
3. To serve, fill glasses with ice cubes if desired. Pour the cranberry spritz over the ice and garnish with lime slices and fresh cranberries.
4. Enjoy immediately for the best fizz and freshness.

Nutritional Information:

Per serving: 50 calories, 0g protein, 12g carbohydrates, 0g fat, 0g fiber, 0mg cholesterol, 10mg sodium, 100mg potassium, 15mg phosphorus.

10. Golden Turmeric Almond Bliss

Yield: 4 servings | Prep Time: 5 minutes | Cook Time: 10 minutes

Ingredients:

- 4 cups almond milk
- 2 teaspoons turmeric powder
- 1 teaspoon cinnamon
- 2 tablespoons honey

Directions:

1. Pour almond milk into a saucepan and heat over medium heat until it's warm but not boiling.
2. Stir in the turmeric and cinnamon. Keep stirring to ensure the mixture is well combined.
3. Add honey to sweeten the mixture. Stir until the honey is fully dissolved.
4. Once the mixture is hot and flavors are well blended, remove from heat.
5. Divide the mixture into serving cups.

Nutritional Information:

Approximately 60 calories, 1g protein, 8g carbohydrates, 2.5g fat, 1g fiber, 0mg cholesterol, 80mg sodium, 150mg potassium, 80mg phosphorus.

11. Chilled Melon Soup

Yield: 4 servings | Prep Time: 15 minutes |
Cook Time: 0 minutes

Ingredients:

- 4 cups cantaloupe, cubed
- Juice of 1 lime
- A handful of fresh mint leaves
- 1 cup ice cubes (optional for immediate serving)
- Fresh mint sprigs for garnish

Directions:

1. In a blender, combine the cubed cantaloupe, lime juice, and mint leaves. Blend until smooth.
2. If a thinner consistency is desired, add a little water to adjust. Taste and adjust the lime juice if needed for extra tanginess.
3. Chill the soup in the refrigerator for at least 1 hour before serving. Serve cold, garnished with fresh mint sprigs. For an immediate cold serving, blend with ice cubes.
4. Optional: For individuals who can include a bit more protein in their diet, consider adding a dollop of Greek yogurt as a garnish before serving.

Nutritional Information:

Per serving: 54 calories, 1g protein, 13g carbohydrates, 0g fat, 1g fiber, 0g cholesterol, 25 mg sodium, 422 mg potassium, 23 mg phosphorus.

12 Kidney-Friendly Green Detox Smoothie

Yield: 4 servings | Prep Time: 10 minutes |
Cook Time: 0 minutes

Ingredients:

- 2 cups kale leaves, stems removed (use in moderation to manage potassium levels)
- 1 medium green apple, cored and sliced
- 1 medium cucumber, peeled if not organic
- Juice of 1 lemon

Directions:

1. Wash all produce thoroughly. If you're concerned about potassium levels, you can also blanch the kale for a few minutes to reduce its potassium content. Drain well.
2. In a blender, combine the kale leaves, green apple slices, cucumber, and lemon juice.
3. Blend on high until smooth. If the mixture is too thick, you can add a little water to reach your desired consistency.
4. Taste and adjust the lemon juice if you prefer it more tangy.
5. Serve immediately, or chill in the refrigerator for a refreshing detox drink.

Nutritional Information:

Per serving: 50 calories, 2g protein, 12g carbohydrates, 0g fat, 2g fiber, 0mg cholesterol, 30mg sodium, 200mg potassium, 50mg phosphorus.

13. Soothing Lavender Lemonade

Yield: 4 servings | Prep Time: 10 minutes | Cook Time: 0 minutes

Ingredients:

- 4 cups water
- 1/2 cup fresh lemon juice (about 2-3 large lemons)
- 2 teaspoons dried lavender (culinary grade)
- 3 tablespoons honey or to taste (or a suitable non-potassium sweetener for renal diets)
- Ice cubes

Directions:

1. In a small saucepan, bring 1 cup of water to a simmer. Remove from heat, add the dried lavender, and let it steep for about 5 minutes.
2. Strain the lavender-infused water into a pitcher, discarding the lavender.
3. Stir in the honey (or sweetener) until dissolved.
4. Add the lemon juice and the remaining 3 cups of water to the pitcher. Stir well.
5. Chill the lemonade in the refrigerator until cold. Serve over ice cubes.

Nutritional Information:

Per serving: 60 calories, 0g protein, 16g carbohydrates, 0g fat, 0g fiber, 0mg cholesterol, 5mg sodium, 50mg potassium, 10mg phosphorus.

14. Avocado & Matcha Energy Smoothie

Yield: 2 servings | Prep Time: 5 minutes | Cook Time: 0 minutes

Ingredients:

- 1/2 ripe avocado
- 1 teaspoon matcha powder
- 1 cup unsweetened almond milk
- 1/2 teaspoon vanilla extract
- Stevia or another non-nutritive sweetener, to taste
- Ice cubes, optional

Directions:

1. Scoop out the avocado flesh and place it in a blender.
2. Add the matcha powder, almond milk, vanilla extract, and sweetener to the blender.
3. Blend on high until smooth and creamy. Add ice cubes if a colder smoothie is desired and blend again.
4. Taste and adjust sweetness, if necessary.
5. Serve immediately for a refreshing and energizing drink.

Nutritional Information:

Per serving: 120 calories, 2g protein, 8g carbohydrates, 10g fat, 4g fiber, 0mg cholesterol, 40mg sodium, 250mg potassium, 50mg phosphorus.

15. Creamy Vanilla Protein Shake

Yield: 2 servings | Prep Time: 5 minutes | Cook Time: 0 minutes

Ingredients:

- 1 cup low-fat Greek yogurt (ensure it's low in phosphorus)
- 2 scoops low-phosphorus vanilla protein powder
- 1 cup unsweetened almond milk
- Ice cubes (optional, for desired consistency)

Directions:

1. Place the Greek yogurt, vanilla protein powder, and almond milk into a blender.
2. Add ice cubes to preference.
3. Blend until smooth and creamy.
4. Pour into glasses and serve immediately.

Nutritional Information:

Per serving: **:** 150 calories, 20g protein, 8g carbohydrates, 3g fat, 1g fiber, 10mg cholesterol, 120mg sodium, 200mg potassium, 100mg phosphorus.

16. Refreshing Berry Watermelon Slush

Yield: 4 servings | Prep Time: 10 minutes | Cook Time: 0 minutes

Ingredients:

- 2 cups cubed watermelon
- 1 cup fresh strawberries, hulled
- Juice of 1 lime
- 2 cups ice

Directions:

1. Place watermelon, strawberries, and lime juice in a blender.
2. Add ice to the blender.
3. Blend on high until smooth and slushy.
4. Serve immediately in chilled glasses.

Nutritional Information:

Per serving: 50 calories, 1g protein, 12g carbohydrates, 0g fat, 1g fiber, 0mg cholesterol, 5mg sodium, 170mg potassium, 20mg phosphorus.

Vegetable Virtues: 14 Vibrant Vegetarian Creations

1. Vegan Shepherd's Pie

Yield: 4 servings | Prep Time: 20 minutes | Cook Time: 30 minutes

Ingredients:

- Lentils
- Sweet potatoes, mashed
- Olive oil
- Onion, diced
- Carrots, diced
- Peas
- Low-sodium vegetable broth
- Rosemary and thyme

Directions:

1. Preheat your oven and prepare a baking dish.
2. Cook lentils as per instructions and mash sweet potatoes.
3. Sauté onions, carrots, and garlic in olive oil until softened.
4. Mix lentils, veggies, and mashed sweet potatoes together with herbs.
5. Transfer the mixture to the baking dish, top with more herbs, and bake until golden.

Nutritional Information:

Per serving: 250 calories, 10g protein, 45g carbohydrates, 5g fat, 8g fiber, 0mg cholesterol, 220mg sodium, 500mg potassium, 200mg phosphorus.

2. Lentil Tacos

Yield: 4 servings | Prep Time: 10 minutes | Cook Time: 25 minutes

Ingredients:

- 1 cup dried lentils, rinsed
- 2 1/2 cups water
- 1 tablespoon low-sodium taco seasoning
- 8 small corn tortillas
- 1 ripe avocado, sliced
- 2 cups shredded lettuce
- 1 large tomato, diced

Directions:

1. In a medium saucepan, combine the lentils and water. Bring to a boil, then reduce the heat to low, cover, and simmer for 20-25 minutes, or until the lentils are tender and the water is absorbed. Remove from heat and stir in the taco seasoning.
2. Warm the corn tortillas in a dry skillet over medium heat for about 30 seconds on each side or until soft and warm.
3. To assemble the tacos, divide the seasoned lentils among the warm tortillas. Top each taco with sliced avocado, shredded lettuce, and diced tomato.
4. Serve immediately, allowing each person to customize their tacos with additional toppings if desired.

Nutritional Information:

Per serving: 255 calories, 13g protein, 40g carbohydrates, 6g fat, 10g fiber, 0mg cholesterol, 200mg sodium, 610mg potassium, 230mg phosphorus.

3. Broccoli and Almond Stir-Fry

Yield: 4 servings | Prep time: 10 minutes |
Cook time: 15 minutes

Ingredients:

- 4 cups broccoli florets
- 1/2 cup sliced almonds
- 2 tablespoons olive oil
- 2 cloves garlic, minced
- 2 tablespoons low-sodium soy sauce
- 1 teaspoon grated ginger
- Sesame seeds (for garnish)

Directions:

1. Prepare the Ingredients: Heat olive oil in a large pan over medium heat. Add garlic and ginger, sautéing until aromatic.
2. Cook Broccoli: Increase heat to medium-high, add broccoli florets, and stir-fry for about 5 minutes, or until they begin to soften and turn bright green.
3. Add Almonds and Season: Incorporate sliced almonds and low-sodium soy sauce into the pan, continuing to stir-fry for another 5-10 minutes until broccoli is tender but still crisp.
4. Garnish and Serve: Transfer to a serving dish, sprinkle with sesame seeds as garnish, and serve warm.

Nutritional Information:

Per serving: 220 calories, 12g protein,
15g carbohydrates, 12g fat, 3g fiber,
0mg cholesterol, 200mg sodium,
400mg potassium, 150mg phosphorus.

4. Kale and White Bean Soup

Yield: 4 servings | Prep Time: 15 minutes |
Cook Time: 30 minutes

Ingredients:

- 4 cups chopped kale, stems removed
- 1 can (15 ounces) white beans, rinsed and drained
- 2 medium carrots, peeled and diced
- 2 celery stalks, diced
- 1 large onion, diced
- 4 cups low-sodium vegetable broth
- 1 teaspoon dried thyme
- Salt and pepper to taste (minimal salt for low sodium)

Directions:

1. In a large pot, heat a splash of water or vegetable broth over medium heat. Add the diced onion, carrots, and celery. Sauté until the vegetables are softened, about 5 minutes.
2. Add the chopped kale to the pot and cook until it starts to wilt, approximately 3-5 minutes.
3. Stir in the white beans, low-sodium vegetable broth, and dried thyme. Season with a pinch of salt and pepper to taste.
4. Bring the soup to a boil, then reduce the heat to a simmer. Cover and let it cook for about 20 minutes, or until the vegetables are tender.
5. Serve hot, adjusting seasoning if necessary.

Nutritional Information:

Per serving: 180 calories, 10g protein,
30g carbohydrates, 1g fat, 8g fiber,
0mg cholesterol, 200mg sodium,
400mg potassium, 100mg phosphorus.

5. Tofu Stir-Fry with Vegetables

Yield: 4 servings | Prep Time: 15 minutes | Cook Time: 15 minutes

Ingredients:

- 14 ounces firm tofu, drained and pressed, cut into cubes
- 4 cups mixed vegetables (e.g., bell peppers, broccoli, snap peas, carrots), chopped
- 2 tablespoons low-sodium soy sauce
- 1 tablespoon olive oil
- 2 cloves garlic, minced
- 1 tablespoon fresh ginger, grated

Directions:

1. Heat olive oil in a large skillet or wok over medium-high heat. Add garlic and ginger, and sauté for about 1 minute until fragrant.
2. Add the mixed vegetables to the skillet and stir-fry for about 5-7 minutes, or until they are just tender.
3. Add the tofu cubes and low-sodium soy sauce to the skillet. Stir gently to combine and cook for another 5-8 minutes, until the tofu is heated through and vegetables are cooked to your liking.
4. Serve hot, optionally over a bed of cooked rice or quinoa for a more filling meal.

Nutritional Information:

Per serving: 205 calories, 13g protein, 16g carbohydrates, 9g fat, 4g fiber, 0mg cholesterol, 210mg sodium, 410mg potassium, 160mg phosphorus.

6. Vegetable Curry with Coconut Milk

Yield: 4 servings | Prep Time: 15 minutes | Cook Time: 30 minutes

Ingredients:

- 4 cups mixed vegetables (e.g., cauliflower, carrots, green beans, bell peppers), chopped
- 1 can (14 ounces) light coconut milk
- 2 tablespoons curry powder
- 1 cup uncooked rice
- 1 tablespoon olive oil
- 1 medium onion, diced
- 2 cloves garlic, minced
- Salt to taste (keeping sodium in mind)

Directions:

1. Cook rice according to package instructions. Set aside and keep warm.
2. In a large skillet or saucepan, heat olive oil over medium heat. Add the onion and garlic, sautéing until the onion is translucent.
3. Add the mixed vegetables to the skillet and cook for about 5 minutes, stirring occasionally.
4. Stir in the curry powder, then add the coconut milk and a pinch of salt. Bring the mixture to a simmer, reduce the heat to low, and cover. Cook for 20 minutes, or until the vegetables are tender.
5. Serve the vegetable curry over the cooked rice.

Nutritional Information:

Per serving: 285 calories, 7g protein, 41g carbohydrates, 12g fat, 6g fiber, 0mg cholesterol, 185mg sodium, 610mg potassium, 210mg phosphorus.

7. Mushroom Risotto

Yield: 4 servings | Prep Time: 10 minutes | Cook Time: 35 minutes

Ingredients:

- 1 cup Arborio rice
- 3 cups sliced mushrooms (e.g., cremini, button)
- 1 small onion, finely chopped
- 4 cups low-sodium vegetable broth, kept warm
- 1/2 cup grated Parmesan cheese
- 2 tablespoons olive oil
- Salt and pepper to taste (keeping sodium in mind)

Directions:

1. In a large saucepan, heat 1 tablespoon of olive oil over medium heat. Add the onion and sauté until translucent, about 5 minutes. Add the mushrooms and cook until they are soft, about 5 minutes more.
2. Add the Arborio rice to the saucepan, stirring for about 1 minute until the grains are well-coated and slightly translucent.
3. Begin adding the warm vegetable broth one ladle at a time, stirring frequently. Wait until the liquid is almost fully absorbed before adding the next ladle. Continue this process until the rice is creamy and al dente, about 25 minutes.
4. Remove from heat and stir in the Parmesan cheese. Season with salt and pepper to taste.
5. Serve immediately, garnished with a little more Parmesan if desired.

Nutritional Information:

Per serving: 305 calories, 9g protein, 51g carbohydrates, 8g fat, 3g fiber, 11mg cholesterol, 205mg sodium, 360mg potassium, 255mg phosphorus.

8. Zucchini Noodles with Tomato Sauce

Yield: 4 servings | Prep Time: 15 minutes | Cook Time: 10 minutes

Ingredients:

- 4 large zucchinis
- 2 cups low-sodium tomato sauce
- 2 tablespoons olive oil
- 2 cloves garlic, minced

Directions:

1. Use a spiralizer to turn the zucchinis into noodles. If you don't have a spiralizer, use a vegetable peeler to create thin zucchini ribbons.
2. Heat olive oil in a large skillet over medium heat. Add the minced garlic and sauté for 1-2 minutes until fragrant.
3. Add the zucchini noodles to the skillet, tossing gently for about 2-3 minutes until just tender. Be careful not to overcook to keep them al dente.
4. Warm the low-sodium tomato sauce in a separate saucepan or in the microwave. Pour the sauce over the cooked zucchini noodles, tossing to coat evenly.
5. Serve immediately, offering additional garnishes like fresh basil or grated Parmesan if desired, while keeping the renal diet in mind.

Nutritional Information:

Per serving: 125 calories, 4g protein, 16g carbohydrates, 7g fat, 5g fiber, 0mg cholesterol, 105mg sodium, 410mg potassium, 110mg phosphorus.

9. Chickpea Salad Sandwich

Yield: 4 servings | Prep Time: 15 minutes |
Cook Time: 0 minutes

Ingredients:

- 1 can (15 ounces) chickpeas, rinsed and drained
- 1/2 cup celery, finely chopped
- 1/4 cup low-fat mayonnaise
- 8 slices whole grain bread
- Salt and pepper to taste (keeping sodium in mind)

Directions:

1. In a medium bowl, mash the chickpeas with a fork or potato masher until coarsely mashed.
2. Mix in the celery and low-fat mayonnaise. Season with salt and pepper to taste. Mix until well combined.
3. Spread the chickpea salad evenly onto 4 slices of whole grain bread. Top each with another slice of bread.
4. Cut sandwiches in half if desired and serve immediately.

Nutritional Information:

Per serving: 255 calories, 11g protein, 37g carbohydrates, 8g fat, 7g fiber, 0mg cholesterol, 310mg sodium, 410mg potassium, 210mg phosphorus.

10. Spaghetti Squash Primavera

Yield: 4 servings | Prep Time: 15 minutes |
Cook Time: 40 minutes

Ingredients:

- Spaghetti squash
- Mixed vegetables (carrots, bell peppers, peas)
- Olive oil
- Garlic, minced
- Low-sodium vegetable broth
- Dried Italian herbs

Directions:

1. Preheat your oven and halve the spaghetti squash, removing seeds.
2. Roast squash until tender.
3. Sauté mixed vegetables and garlic in olive oil.
4. Add vegetable broth and Italian herbs to the sautéed vegetables.
5. Scrape spaghetti squash into strands and mix with the sautéed vegetables.

Nutritional Information:

Per serving: 200 calories, 5g protein, 30g carbohydrates, 7g fat, 6g fiber, 0mg cholesterol, 180mg sodium, 400mg potassium, 100mg phosphorus.

11. Roasted Vegetable Quiche

Yield: 4 servings | Prep Time: 20 minutes |
Cook Time: 40 minutes

Ingredients:

- 1 premade pie crust
- 4 eggs
- 1 cup low-fat milk
- 2 cups mixed roasted vegetables (bell peppers, onions, zucchini), cooled
- 1 cup shredded low-sodium cheese (such as mozzarella or Swiss)
- 1 tablespoon mixed herbs (such as thyme, oregano, and basil), finely chopped
- Salt and pepper to taste (minimal salt for low sodium)

Directions:

1. Preheat the oven to 375°F (190°C). Place the pie crust in a 9-inch pie dish and set aside.
2. In a large bowl, whisk together the eggs, low-fat milk, and mixed herbs. Season lightly with salt and pepper.
3. Stir in the roasted vegetables and shredded low-sodium cheese until well combined.
4. Pour the egg and vegetable mixture into the prepared pie crust, spreading the vegetables evenly.
5. Bake in the preheated oven for 35-40 minutes, or until the quiche is set and the crust is golden brown.
6. Let the quiche cool for a few minutes before slicing and serving. Can be enjoyed warm or at room temperature.

Nutritional Information:

Per serving: 230 calories, 11g protein, 22g carbohydrates, 12g fat, 3g fiber, 120mg cholesterol, 180mg sodium, 350mg potassium, 180mg phosphorus.

12. Stuffed Acorn Squash

Yield: 4 servings | Prep Time: 15 minutes |
Cook Time: 45 minutes

Ingredients:

- 2 acorn squashes, halved and seeded
- 1 cup cooked wild rice
- 1/2 cup dried cranberries
- 1/2 cup chopped walnuts
- 2 tablespoons maple syrup
- 1/2 teaspoon cinnamon

Directions:

1. Preheat the oven to 375°F (190°C). Place the acorn squash halves cut-side up on a baking sheet. Bake for about 25-30 minutes, or until the squash is tender.
2. While the squash is baking, mix the cooked wild rice, dried cranberries, chopped walnuts, maple syrup, and cinnamon in a bowl.
3. Once the squash is tender, remove it from the oven and fill each half with the wild rice mixture.
4. Return the stuffed squash to the oven and bake for an additional 15 minutes, or until the filling is heated through.
5. Serve warm, drizzled with additional maple syrup if desired.

Nutritional Information:

Per serving: 210 calories, 4g protein, 45g carbohydrates, 3g fat, 5g fiber, 0mg cholesterol, 30mg sodium, 500mg potassium, 150mg phosphorus.

13. Vegetarian Chili

Yield: 4 servings | Prep Time: 10 minutes | Cook Time: 30 minutes

Ingredients:

- 1 can (15 ounces) kidney beans, rinsed and drained
- 1 can (15 ounces) black beans, rinsed and drained
- 1 can (28 ounces) tomatoes, diced
- 1 large bell pepper, diced
- 1 large onion, diced
- 2 tablespoons chili powder
- 1 teaspoon cumin
- Salt and pepper to taste (minimal salt for low sodium)

Directions:

1. In a large pot, heat a splash of water or vegetable broth over medium heat. Add the diced onion and bell pepper, and sauté until softened, about 5 minutes.
2. Stir in the chili powder and cumin, cooking for another minute until fragrant.
3. Add the kidney beans, black beans, and diced tomatoes (with their juice) to the pot. Stir to combine.
4. Bring the chili to a boil, then reduce the heat and simmer, uncovered, for about 25 minutes, allowing the flavors to meld and the chili to thicken. Stir occasionally.
5. Season with salt and pepper to taste. Serve hot, with optional toppings like low-fat sour cream, shredded cheese, or fresh cilantro if desired.

Nutritional Information:

Per serving: 240 calories, 13g protein, 45g carbohydrates, 1g fat, 12g fiber, 0mg cholesterol, 200mg sodium, 700mg potassium, 250mg phosphorus.

14. Sweet Potato and Black Bean Enchiladas

Yield: 4 servings | Prep Time: 20 minutes | Cook Time: 30 minutes

Ingredients:

- 2 medium sweet potatoes, peeled and diced
- 1 can (15 ounces) black beans, rinsed and drained
- 8 whole wheat tortillas
- 1 cup enchilada sauce (low-sodium)
- 1 cup shredded low-sodium cheese (such as mozzarella or cheddar)
- 1 ripe avocado, sliced
- Fresh cilantro for garnish (optional)

Directions:

1. Preheat the oven to 375°F (190°C). Boil the sweet potatoes in water until tender, about 10-15 minutes. Drain and set aside.
2. In a mixing bowl, combine the cooked sweet potatoes and black beans. Mash lightly with a fork, leaving some texture.
3. Spread a thin layer of enchilada sauce on the bottom of a baking dish.
4. Fill each tortilla with the sweet potato and black bean mixture, roll tightly, and place seam-side down in the baking dish.
5. Pour the remaining enchilada sauce over the rolled tortillas and sprinkle with shredded cheese.
6. Bake in the preheated oven for about 20 minutes, or until the cheese is melted and bubbly.
7. Serve hot, garnished with sliced avocado and fresh cilantro if desired.

Nutritional Information:

Per serving: 350 calories, 12g protein, 55g carbohydrates, 9g fat, 10g fiber, 20mg cholesterol, 280mg sodium, 600mg potassium, 220mg phosphorus.

Ocean's Bounty: 14 Captivating Seafood Dishes

1. Grilled Rainbow Trout with Herb Salad

Yield: 4 servings | Prep time: 15 minutes | Cook time: 10 minutes

Ingredients:

- 4 rainbow trout fillets
- 1 cup mixed herbs (parsley, cilantro, dill), chopped
- 2 tablespoons lemon juice
- 3 tablespoons olive oil
- Salt (minimal, for low sodium) and pepper to taste

Directions:

1. Preheat your grill to medium-high heat. Rinse the trout fillets and pat dry.
2. In a small bowl, mix lemon juice, 2 tablespoons olive oil, salt, and pepper. Brush this mixture over both sides of the trout fillets.
3. Grill the trout fillets, skin side down, covered, for about 5-7 minutes or until the fish flakes easily with a fork.
4. In a separate bowl, toss the mixed herbs with the remaining 1 tablespoon of olive oil and a squeeze of lemon juice. Season with a pinch of salt and pepper.
5. Serve the grilled trout topped with the fresh herb salad.

Nutritional Information:

Per serving: 200 calories, 22g protein, 1g carbohydrates, 12g fat, 0g fiber, 60mg cholesterol, 70mg sodium, 300mg potassium, 200mg phosphorus.

2. Garlic Herb Shrimp Skewers

Yield: 4 servings | Prep time: 15 minutes | Cook time: 6 minutes

Ingredients:

- 1 pound large shrimp, peeled and deveined
- 4 cloves garlic, minced
- 2 tablespoons fresh parsley, finely chopped
- 1 tablespoon fresh thyme, finely chopped
- 3 tablespoons olive oil
- Salt and pepper to taste (use salt sparingly for low sodium)

Directions:

1. In a bowl, combine the shrimp, garlic, parsley, thyme, and olive oil. Season with a pinch of salt and pepper. Toss to coat the shrimp evenly.
2. Thread the shrimp onto skewers. If using wooden skewers, soak them in water for at least 30 minutes before grilling to prevent burning.
3. Preheat a grill or grill pan over medium-high heat. Grill the shrimp skewers for 2-3 minutes on each side, or until the shrimp are opaque and cooked through.
4. Serve immediately, garnished with additional parsley and lemon wedges if desired.

Nutritional Information:

Per serving: 220 calories, 24g protein, 1g carbohydrates, 13g fat, 0g fiber, 180mg cholesterol, 150mg sodium, 200mg potassium, 220mg phosphorus.

3. Baked Cod with Paprika

Yield: 4 servings | Prep time: 10 minutes | Cook time: 15 minutes

Ingredients:

- 4 cod fillets (6 ounces each)
- 1 tablespoon smoked paprika
- Zest of 1 lemon
- 2 tablespoons olive oil
- Salt and pepper to taste (use salt sparingly for moderate sodium)

Directions:

1. Preheat the oven to 400°F (200°C). Line a baking sheet with parchment paper.
2. Place the cod fillets on the prepared baking sheet. Drizzle with olive oil and season with smoked paprika, lemon zest, and a pinch of salt and pepper. Rub the seasoning onto both sides of the fillets.
3. Bake in the preheated oven for 12-15 minutes, or until the cod is flaky and cooked through.
4. Serve immediately, garnished with lemon wedges if desired.

Nutritional Information:

Per serving: 200 calories, 25g protein, 0g carbohydrates, 10g fat, 0g fiber, 60mg cholesterol, 180mg sodium, 300mg potassium, 250mg phosphorus.

4. Tuna and Avocado Salad

Yield: 4 servings | Prep time: 15 minutes | Cook time: 0 minutes

Ingredients:

- 2 cans (5 ounces each) tuna in water, drained
- 2 ripe avocados, peeled and diced
- Juice of 1 lemon
- 1/4 cup red onion, finely chopped
- Salt and pepper to taste (use salt sparingly for low sodium)

Directions:

1. In a large bowl, combine the drained tuna, diced avocado, lemon juice, and red onion. Gently mix to combine without mashing the avocado too much.
2. Season with a pinch of salt and pepper to taste. Mix again lightly.
3. Let the salad chill in the refrigerator for about 10 minutes before serving to allow the flavors to meld.
4. Serve chilled, alone, or as a filling for a wrap or sandwich.

Nutritional Information:

Per serving: 230 calories, 20g protein, 9g carbohydrates, 14g fat, 7g fiber, 30mg cholesterol, 180mg sodium, 500mg potassium, 150mg phosphorus.

5. Pan-Seared Scallops with Asparagus

Yield: 4 servings | Prep time: 10 minutes | Cook time: 15 minutes

Ingredients:

- 12 large scallops, patted dry
- 1 pound asparagus, ends trimmed
- 2 cloves garlic, minced
- Juice of 1 lemon
- 2 tablespoons olive oil
- Salt and pepper to taste (use salt sparingly for low sodium)

Directions:

1. Heat 1 tablespoon of olive oil in a large skillet over medium-high heat. Season the scallops with a pinch of salt and pepper, then add them to the skillet. Sear for about 2 minutes on each side or until a golden crust forms and scallops are cooked through. Remove from the skillet and set aside.
2. In the same skillet, add the remaining tablespoon of olive oil and garlic, sautéing for 1 minute. Add the asparagus and cook for about 5 minutes, or until tender but still crisp. Season with a pinch of salt and pepper.
3. Return the scallops to the skillet, squeeze lemon juice over the top, and toss gently to combine.
4. Serve immediately, garnishing with additional lemon wedges if desired.

Nutritional Information:

Per serving: 190 calories, 18g protein, 8g carbohydrates, 10g fat, 3g fiber, 40mg cholesterol, 220mg sodium, 350mg potassium, 200mg phosphorus.

6. Grilled Tilapia with Mango Salsa

Yield: 4 servings | Prep time: 20 minutes | Cook time: 10 minutes

Ingredients:

- 4 tilapia fillets (6 ounces each)
- 1 ripe mango, diced
- 1 red bell pepper, diced
- 1/4 cup cilantro, finely chopped
- Juice of 1 lime
- 2 tablespoons olive oil
- Salt and pepper to taste (use salt sparingly for low sodium)

Directions:

1. Preheat grill to medium-high heat. Brush tilapia fillets with 1 tablespoon olive oil and season lightly with salt and pepper.
2. Grill tilapia for about 4-5 minutes on each side, or until the fish flakes easily with a fork.
3. In a medium bowl, combine diced mango, red bell pepper, cilantro, lime juice, and the remaining tablespoon of olive oil. Season with a pinch of salt and mix well to create the salsa.
4. Serve the grilled tilapia topped with the mango salsa.

Nutritional Information:

Per serving: 220 calories, 23g protein, 15g carbohydrates, 8g fat, 2g fiber, 55mg cholesterol, 150mg sodium, 450mg potassium, 210mg phosphorus.

7. Crab Cakes with Yogurt Dipping Sauce

Yield: 4 servings | Prep time: 20 minutes |
Cook time: 10 minutes

Ingredients:

- 1 pound lump crab meat, carefully checked for shells
- 1 cup breadcrumbs, whole grain if possible
- 1/2 cup Greek yogurt, low-fat
- 1/4 cup chives, finely chopped, plus extra for garnish
- 1 tablespoon Dijon mustard
- 1 egg, lightly beaten
- 2 tablespoons olive oil for frying
- Salt and pepper to taste (use salt sparingly for low sodium)
- Yogurt Dipping Sauce:
- 1/2 cup Greek yogurt, low-fat
- 2 tablespoons chives, chopped
- 1 tablespoon lemon juice
- Salt and pepper to taste (use salt sparingly for low sodium)

Directions:

1. In a large bowl, combine crab meat, breadcrumbs, 1/2 cup Greek yogurt, chives, Dijon mustard, and beaten egg. Season with a pinch of salt and pepper. Mix gently until well combined.
2. Form the mixture into 8 crab cakes, about 1/2 inch thick.
3. Heat olive oil in a large skillet over medium heat. Cook crab cakes for about 5 minutes on each side, or until golden brown and heated through.
4. For the yogurt dipping sauce, mix 1/2 cup Greek yogurt, chives, and lemon juice in a small bowl. Season with a pinch of salt and pepper to taste.
5. Serve crab cakes hot with yogurt dipping sauce on the side, garnished with additional chives.

Nutritional Information:

250 calories, 24g protein, 18g carbohydrates, 9g fat, 1g fiber, 95mg cholesterol, 200mg sodium, 350mg potassium, 250mg phosphorus.

8. Clam Chowder Light

Yield: 4 servings | Prep time: 15 minutes |
Cook time: 30 minutes

Ingredients:

- 2 cans (6.5 ounces each) low sodium clams, juice reserved
- 2 medium potatoes, peeled and diced
- 1 cup celery, chopped
- 1 medium onion, chopped
- 2 cups skim milk
- 2 tablespoons all-purpose flour
- 2 tablespoons unsalted butter
- Salt and pepper to taste (use salt sparingly for minimal sodium)

Directions:

1. In a large pot, melt butter over medium heat. Add onion and celery, and sauté until they are soft, about 5 minutes.
2. Sprinkle flour over the vegetables and stir to combine. Cook for 2 minutes to remove the raw flour taste.
3. Gradually add the reserved clam juice, stirring constantly to prevent lumps. Add the diced potatoes and bring to a simmer. Cook until the potatoes are tender, about 15 minutes.
4. Stir in the clams and skim milk, and heat through without boiling to prevent the milk from curdling. Season with a pinch of salt and pepper.
5. Serve hot, garnished with fresh parsley if desired.

Nutritional Information:

Per serving: 210 calories, 16g protein, 30g carbohydrates, 3g fat, 2g fiber, 22mg cholesterol, 150mg sodium, 500mg potassium, 180mg phosphorus.

9. Baked Flounder with Lemon Garlic

Yield: 4 servings | Prep Time: 10 minutes |
Cook Time: 20 minutes

Ingredients:

- 4 flounder fillets
- 4 garlic cloves, minced
- Juice of 1 lemon
- 2 tablespoons chopped parsley

Directions:

1. Preheat your oven to 375°F (190°C). Line a baking tray with parchment paper.
2. Arrange flounder fillets on the tray. Drizzle with lemon juice and sprinkle with minced garlic.
3. Bake for 15-20 minutes, or until the fish flakes easily with a fork.
4. Garnish with fresh parsley before serving.

Nutritional Information:

Per serving: 200 calories, 25g protein, 3g carbohydrates, 5g fat, 1g fiber, 60mg cholesterol, 75mg sodium, 500mg potassium, 250mg phosphorus.

10. Seafood Paella (Renal-Friendly)

Yield: 4 servings | Prep Time: 20 minutes |
Cook Time: 40 minutes

Ingredients:

- 1 cup rice (short-grain or paella rice)
- 4 cups low-sodium chicken broth
- 1/2 pound shrimp, peeled and deveined
- 1/2 pound mussels, cleaned and debearded
- 1 pinch saffron threads
- 1 red bell pepper, sliced
- 1 yellow bell pepper, sliced
- 2 tablespoons olive oil
- 1 onion, finely chopped
- 2 cloves garlic, minced
- Salt and pepper to taste (use salt sparingly for low sodium)
- Lemon wedges for serving

Directions:

1. Heat olive oil in a large paella pan or wide skillet over medium heat. Add onion and garlic, and sauté until soft.
2. Add rice to the pan, stirring to coat with oil. Add saffron and stir for about 1 minute. Pour in the low-sodium chicken broth, bring to a simmer, and cook for 10 minutes, uncovered.
3. Arrange shrimp, mussels, and bell peppers on top of the rice. Cover and cook for 20-25 minutes or until the seafood is cooked and rice is tender. Season with a pinch of salt and pepper.
4. Remove from heat and let it stand for 5 minutes, covered. Serve with lemon wedges on the side.

Nutritional Information:

Per serving: 350 calories, 25g protein, 50g carbohydrates, 8g fat, 3g fiber, 120mg cholesterol, 220mg sodium, 500mg potassium, 300mg phosphorus.

11. Poached Pear Grouper

Yield: 4 servings | Prep Time: 15 minutes | Cook Time: 25 minutes

Ingredients:

- 4 grouper fillets (6 ounces each)
- 2 pears, peeled and sliced
- 1 cup white wine vinegar
- 2 cups water
- 1 tablespoon fresh thyme, chopped
- Salt and pepper to taste (use salt sparingly for low sodium)

Directions:

1. In a large skillet, combine white wine vinegar, water, and half of the thyme. Bring to a simmer over medium heat.
2. Season the grouper fillets with a pinch of salt and pepper. Add the fillets and pear slices to the simmering liquid. Cover and poach for about 15-20 minutes, or until the fish is opaque and cooked through.
3. Carefully remove the grouper and pears from the liquid with a slotted spoon. Arrange on plates and garnish with the remaining fresh thyme.
4. Reduce the poaching liquid by half over high heat and drizzle over the fish and pears before serving.

Nutritional Information:

Per serving: 220 calories, 24g protein, 15g carbohydrates, 6g fat, 3g fiber, 60mg cholesterol, 150mg sodium, 550mg potassium, 250mg phosphorus.

12. Mediterranean Haddock Packet

Yield: 4 servings | Prep Time: 15 minutes | Cook Time: 20 minutes

Ingredients:

- 4 haddock fillets (6 ounces each)
- 1 cup cherry tomatoes, halved
- 1/2 cup olives, pitted and sliced
- 1/2 cup feta cheese, crumbled
- 2 teaspoons dried oregano
- 4 tablespoons olive oil
- Salt and pepper to taste (use salt sparingly for reduced sodium)
- 4 lemon wedges for serving

Directions:

1. Preheat the oven to 400°F (200°C). Cut four large pieces of parchment paper or aluminum foil, enough to wrap each fillet comfortably.
2. Place a haddock fillet on each piece of parchment or foil. Drizzle each fillet with 1 tablespoon of olive oil. Season lightly with salt and pepper.
3. Divide the cherry tomatoes, olives, feta cheese, and oregano evenly among the packets, scattering them around the fish.
4. Fold the parchment or foil over the fish and vegetables, sealing the edges to form a packet. Place the packets on a baking sheet.
5. Bake for about 20 minutes, or until the fish is opaque and flakes easily with a fork.
6. Carefully open the packets (watch for steam) and serve immediately, with a lemon wedge for squeezing over the fish.

Nutritional Information:

Per serving: 280 calories, 26g protein, 6g carbohydrates, 16g fat, 2g fiber, 80mg cholesterol, 220mg sodium, 450mg potassium, 270mg phosphorus.

13. Shrimp and Grits Light

Yield: 4 servings | Prep Time: 10 minutes | Cook Time: 20 minutes

Ingredients:

- 1 pound shrimp, peeled and deveined
- 3 cups low-sodium chicken broth
- 1 cup corn grits (polenta)
- 1/2 cup green onions, chopped
- 1 tablespoon olive oil
- Salt and pepper to taste (use salt sparingly for low sodium)

Directions:

1. Bring the low-sodium chicken broth to a boil in a medium saucepan. Gradually whisk in the corn grits. Reduce the heat to low, cover, and simmer, stirring occasionally, until the grits are thick and creamy, about 15-20 minutes.
2. While the grits are cooking, heat olive oil in a large skillet over medium heat. Add the shrimp and cook until they are pink and opaque, about 3-4 minutes per side. Season with a pinch of salt and pepper.
3. Stir half of the green onions into the cooked grits and save the rest for garnishing.
4. To serve, spoon the grits into bowls and top with the cooked shrimp. Garnish with the remaining green onions.

Nutritional Information:

Per serving: 310 calories, 28g protein, 35g carbohydrates, 7g fat, 2g fiber, 180mg cholesterol, 190mg sodium, 420mg potassium, 250mg phosphorus.

14. Sole Meunière Over Spinach

Yield: 4 servings | Prep Time: 10 minutes | Cook Time: 10 minutes

Ingredients:

- 4 sole fillets (6 ounces each)
- Juice of 2 lemons
- 2 tablespoons capers, rinsed
- 4 cups fresh spinach
- 2 tablespoons olive oil
- Salt and pepper to taste (use salt sparingly for minimal sodium)

Directions:

1. Heat 1 tablespoon of olive oil in a large skillet over medium heat. Add the spinach and sauté until wilted, about 2-3 minutes. Season with a pinch of salt and pepper. Divide the spinach among four plates.
2. In the same skillet, heat the remaining tablespoon of olive oil over medium-high heat. Season the sole fillets with a pinch of salt and pepper. Cook the sole for 2-3 minutes on each side, or until the fish is opaque and flakes easily with a fork.
3. Remove the sole from the skillet and place on top of the spinach. In the same skillet, add lemon juice and capers. Cook for 1 minute, scraping up any browned bits from the pan. Spoon the lemon caper sauce over the sole and spinach.
4. Serve immediately.

Nutritional Information:

Per serving: 200 calories, 23g protein, 3g carbohydrates, 10g fat, 2g fiber, 55mg cholesterol, 170mg sodium, 450mg potassium, 200mg phosphorus.

Soulful Simmers: 14 Heartening Soup Creations

1. Creamy Cauliflower Soup

Yield: 4 servings | Prep Time: 15 minutes | Cook Time: 25 minutes

Ingredients:

- 1 large cauliflower head, chopped
- 4 cups low-sodium vegetable broth
- 1 medium onion, chopped
- 2 cloves garlic, minced
- 1 teaspoon dried thyme
- 1 teaspoon dried rosemary
- 1 cup skim milk
- Salt and pepper to taste (use salt sparingly for low sodium)
- Olive oil for sautéing

Directions:

1. In a large pot, heat a splash of olive oil over medium heat. Add the onion and garlic, sautéing until soft and translucent, about 5 minutes.
2. Add the chopped cauliflower, thyme, rosemary, and low-sodium vegetable broth. Bring to a boil, then reduce heat and simmer until the cauliflower is tender, about 15-20 minutes.
3. Remove from heat and let cool slightly. Puree the soup in batches in a blender or use an immersion blender in the pot until smooth.
4. Return the soup to the pot (if using a standard blender) and stir in the skim milk. Heat through, but do not boil. Season with salt and pepper to taste.
5. Serve hot, garnished with a sprinkle of herbs or a drizzle of olive oil if desired.

Nutritional Information:

Per serving: 120 calories, 6g protein, 15g carbohydrates, 2g fat, 5g fiber, 1mg cholesterol, 150mg sodium, 400mg potassium, 100mg phosphorus.

2. Carrot Ginger Puree

Yield: 4 servings | Prep Time: 10 minutes | Cook Time: 20 minutes

Ingredients:

- 1 pound carrots, peeled and chopped
- 2 inches fresh ginger, peeled and minced
- 2 cups low-sodium vegetable broth
- 1/4 cup cream
- Salt to taste (use sparingly for minimal sodium)

Directions:

1. In a large pot, combine the carrots, ginger, and low-sodium vegetable broth. Bring to a boil, then reduce heat and simmer until the carrots are very tender, about 20 minutes.
2. Carefully transfer the carrot mixture to a blender, or use an immersion blender in the pot, and puree until smooth.
3. Return the pureed mixture to the pot (if using a standard blender) and stir in the cream. Heat through on low heat, but do not boil. Season with a pinch of salt to taste.
4. Serve the puree hot, garnished with a sprinkle of fresh herbs or a drizzle of cream if desired.

Nutritional Information:

Per serving: 130 calories, 2g protein, 18g carbohydrates, 6g fat, 4g fiber, 20mg cholesterol, 170mg sodium, 360mg potassium, 120mg phosphorus.

3. Hearty Vegetable Stew

Yield: 4 servings | Prep Time: 15 minutes |
Cook Time: 30 minutes

Ingredients:

- 2 cups chopped low-potassium vegetables (e.g., bell peppers, cabbage, zucchini)
- 4 cups low-sodium vegetable broth
- 1/2 cup barley
- 1 onion, chopped
- 2 cloves garlic, minced
- 1 teaspoon dried thyme
- 1 teaspoon dried rosemary
- 1 tablespoon olive oil
- Salt and pepper to taste (use salt sparingly for low sodium)

Directions:

1. Heat olive oil in a large pot over medium heat. Add onion and garlic, and sauté until softened, about 5 minutes.
2. Add the low-potassium vegetables to the pot and cook for another 5 minutes, stirring occasionally.
3. Pour in the low-sodium vegetable broth and bring to a boil. Add the barley, thyme, and rosemary. Reduce heat, cover, and simmer for about 20 minutes, or until the barley is tender and the vegetables are cooked through.
4. Season with a pinch of salt and pepper to taste. Let the stew simmer for an additional 5 minutes to blend the flavors.
5. Serve hot, garnished with fresh herbs if desired.

Nutritional Information:

Per serving: 180 calories, 4g protein, 35g carbohydrates, 3g fat, 8g fiber, 0mg cholesterol, 200mg sodium, 450mg potassium, 150mg phosphorus.

4. Chicken Noodle Soup (Renal-Friendly)

Yield: 4 servings | Prep Time: 15 minutes |
Cook Time: 25 minutes

Ingredients:

- 4 cups low-sodium chicken broth
- 1 pound chicken breast, cut into bite-sized pieces
- 1 cup carrots, sliced
- 1 cup celery, sliced
- 1 cup low-protein noodles
- 1 tablespoon olive oil
- Salt and pepper to taste (use salt sparingly for low sodium)

Directions:

1. Heat olive oil in a large pot over medium heat. Add the chicken pieces and cook until lightly browned and no longer pink in the middle, about 5-7 minutes. Remove chicken and set aside.
2. In the same pot, add a bit more olive oil if needed, then add the carrots and celery. Sauté until they start to soften, about 5 minutes.
3. Return the chicken to the pot and add the low-sodium chicken broth. Bring to a simmer.
4. Add the low-protein noodles to the pot and cook according to package instructions, usually about 10 minutes, until tender.
5. Season the soup with a pinch of salt and pepper to taste. Serve hot.

Nutritional Information:

Per serving: 220 calories, 26g protein, 22g carbohydrates, 5g fat, 3g fiber, 55mg cholesterol, 180mg sodium, 400mg potassium, 220mg phosphorus.

5. Beef Barley Soup

Yield: 4 servings | Prep Time: 15 minutes | Cook Time: 1 hour

Ingredients:

- 1 pound lean beef, cubed
- 3/4 cup barley
- 6 cups low-sodium beef broth
- 1 cup carrots, diced
- 1 cup celery, diced
- 1 tablespoon olive oil
- Salt and pepper to taste (use salt sparingly for low sodium)

Directions:

1. Heat olive oil in a large pot over medium-high heat. Add the beef cubes and season with a pinch of salt and pepper. Brown the beef on all sides, about 5-7 minutes.
2. Add the low-sodium beef broth to the pot along with the barley. Bring to a boil, then reduce heat to low, cover, and simmer for 45 minutes.
3. Add the carrots and celery to the pot. Continue to simmer, covered, for an additional 15 minutes, or until the vegetables and barley are tender.
4. Adjust seasoning with salt and pepper if needed. Serve hot.

Nutritional Information:

Per serving: 330 calories, 28g protein, 40g carbohydrates, 7g fat, 8g fiber, 60mg cholesterol, 200mg sodium, 500mg potassium, 250mg phosphorus.

6. Lentil and Spinach Soup

Yield: 4 servings | Prep Time: 10 minutes | Cook Time: 30 minutes

Ingredients:

- 1 cup lentils, rinsed
- 4 cups low-sodium vegetable broth
- 2 cups fresh spinach, chopped
- 1 large onion, chopped
- 2 cloves garlic, minced
- 1 tablespoon olive oil
- Salt and pepper to taste (use salt sparingly for low sodium)

Directions:

1. Heat olive oil in a large pot over medium heat. Add the onion and garlic, and sauté until the onion is translucent, about 5 minutes.
2. Add the lentils and low-sodium vegetable broth to the pot. Bring to a boil, then reduce heat to low, cover, and simmer for about 20 minutes, or until the lentils are tender.
3. Add the chopped spinach to the pot and cook for an additional 5 minutes, or until the spinach is wilted.
4. Season the soup with a pinch of salt and pepper to taste. Serve hot.

Nutritional Information:

Per serving: 210 calories, 14g protein, 35g carbohydrates, 3g fat, 15g fiber, 0mg cholesterol, 120mg sodium, 370mg potassium, 180mg phosphorus.

7. Split Pea Soup (Low Sodium)

Yield: 4 servings | Prep Time: 10 minutes | Cook Time: 1 hour 30 minutes

Ingredients:

- 1 cup dried split peas, rinsed
- 4 cups low-sodium vegetable broth
- 1/2 pound low-sodium ham, cubed
- 1 cup carrots, diced
- 1 cup celery, diced
- 1 onion, chopped
- 2 cloves garlic, minced
- 1 teaspoon dried thyme
- 1 bay leaf
- Salt and pepper to taste (use salt sparingly for low sodium)
- Water as needed

Directions:

1. In a large pot, combine split peas, low-sodium vegetable broth, ham, carrots, celery, onion, garlic, thyme, and bay leaf. Add enough water to cover the ingredients by 2 inches.
2. Bring to a boil, then reduce heat to low, cover, and simmer for 1 hour, or until the split peas are soft and the soup has thickened. Stir occasionally and add more water if needed to achieve desired consistency.
3. Remove the bay leaf. Use an immersion blender to puree the soup to your preferred texture, either smooth or leaving some chunks for texture.
4. Season with a pinch of salt and pepper to taste. Serve hot.

Nutritional Information:

Per serving: 250 calories, 19g protein, 35g carbohydrates, 4g fat, 14g fiber, 20mg cholesterol, 200mg sodium, 600mg potassium, 200mg phosphorus.

8. Tomato Basil Soup (Low Potassium)

Yield: 4 servings | Prep Time: 10 minutes | Cook Time: 30 minutes

Ingredients:

- 4 cups chopped low-potassium tomatoes (canned no-salt-added or fresh with low potassium levels)
- 2 cups low-sodium chicken broth
- 1 onion, chopped
- 2 cloves garlic, minced
- 1/4 cup fresh basil leaves, chopped, plus more for garnish
- 1 tablespoon olive oil
- Salt and pepper to taste (use salt sparingly for low sodium)

Directions:

1. Heat olive oil in a large pot over medium heat. Add onion and garlic, sautéing until soft and translucent, about 5 minutes.
2. Add the chopped tomatoes and low-sodium chicken broth to the pot. Bring to a boil, then reduce heat and simmer for 20 minutes.
3. Add the chopped basil leaves to the soup. Use an immersion blender to puree the soup until smooth, or transfer to a blender in batches and blend until smooth.
4. Season the soup with a pinch of salt and pepper to taste. Heat through for an additional 5 minutes.
5. Serve hot, garnished with fresh basil leaves.

Nutritional Information:

Per serving: 90 calories, 4g protein, 13g carbohydrates, 3g fat, 3g fiber, 0mg cholesterol, 150mg sodium, 290mg potassium, 100mg phosphorus.

9. Mushroom Barley Soup

Yield: 4 servings | Prep Time: 15 minutes | Cook Time: 45 minutes

Ingredients:

- 2 cups sliced mushrooms
- 1 cup barley
- 4 cups low-sodium beef broth
- 1 onion, chopped
- 2 cloves garlic, minced
- 1 teaspoon dried thyme
- 1/2 teaspoon dried rosemary
- 2 tablespoons olive oil
- 1/4 cup cream
- Salt and pepper to taste (use salt sparingly for controlled sodium)

Directions:

1. Heat olive oil in a large pot over medium heat. Add the onion and garlic, and sauté until soft, about 5 minutes.
2. Add the mushrooms and cook until they start to brown, about 8 minutes.
3. Stir in the barley, thyme, rosemary, and low-sodium beef broth. Bring to a boil, then reduce the heat to low, cover, and simmer for about 30 minutes, or until the barley is tender.
4. Once the barley is cooked, stir in the cream and heat through for another 5 minutes. Season with a pinch of salt and pepper to taste.
5. Serve hot, garnished with a sprig of rosemary or thyme if desired.

Nutritional Information:

Per serving: 260 calories, 8g protein, 45g carbohydrates, 7g fat, 10g fiber, 20mg cholesterol, 180mg sodium, 400mg potassium, 150mg phosphorus.

10. Minestrone Soup (Renal Adapted)

Yield: 4 servings | Prep Time: 15 minutes | Cook Time: 30 minutes

Ingredients:

- 2 cups mixed low-potassium vegetables (e.g., zucchini, green beans, carrots), chopped
- 1 cup canned beans (e.g., cannellini), rinsed and drained to reduce potassium
- 1/2 cup small pasta (e.g., macaroni or shells)
- 4 cups low-sodium vegetable broth
- 1 onion, chopped
- 2 cloves garlic, minced
- 1 teaspoon dried oregano
- 1 teaspoon dried basil
- 2 tablespoons olive oil
- Salt and pepper to taste (use salt sparingly for low sodium)

Directions:

1. Heat olive oil in a large pot over medium heat. Add the onion and garlic, and sauté until translucent, about 5 minutes.
2. Add the low-sodium vegetable broth, chopped low-potassium vegetables, oregano, and basil. Bring to a boil, then reduce heat and simmer for 15 minutes.
3. Stir in the beans and pasta, and continue to simmer for another 10-15 minutes, or until the pasta is cooked and the vegetables are tender.
4. Season with a pinch of salt and pepper to taste. Serve hot.

Nutritional Information:

Per serving: 220 calories, 10g protein, 35g carbohydrates, 5g fat, 8g fiber, 0mg cholesterol, 180mg sodium, 450mg potassium, 200mg phosphorus.

11. Broccoli and Cheese Soup

Yield: 4 servings | Prep Time: 10 minutes |
Cook Time: 20 minutes

Ingredients:

- 4 cups chopped broccoli
- 2 cups low-sodium vegetable broth
- 1 cup skim milk
- 1 cup shredded low-fat cheddar cheese
- 1 onion, chopped
- 2 cloves garlic, minced
- 2 tablespoons flour
- 2 tablespoons olive oil
- Salt and pepper to taste (use salt sparingly for low sodium)

Directions:

1. Heat olive oil in a large pot over medium heat. Add the onion and garlic, and sauté until translucent, about 5 minutes.
2. Stir in the flour to create a roux, cooking for about 1 minute.
3. Slowly whisk in the low-sodium vegetable broth and skim milk, ensuring there are no lumps. Bring to a simmer.
4. Add the chopped broccoli. Cook until the broccoli is tender, about 10-15 minutes.
5. Reduce the heat to low. Stir in the shredded low-fat cheddar cheese until melted and smooth. Season with a pinch of salt and pepper to taste.
6. Use an immersion blender to slightly puree the soup, leaving some broccoli chunks for texture, if desired.
7. Serve hot.

Nutritional Information:

Per serving: 190 calories, 12g protein,
15g carbohydrates, 9g fat, 4g fiber,
20mg cholesterol, 200mg sodium,
350mg potassium, 180mg phosphorus.

12. Turkey and Rice Soup

Yield: 4 servings | Prep Time: 10 minutes |
Cook Time: 30 minutes

Ingredients:

- 1 pound ground turkey
- 1 cup rice
- 6 cups low-sodium chicken broth
- 1 cup carrots, diced
- 1 cup celery, diced
- 1 tablespoon olive oil
- Salt and pepper to taste (minimal salt for low sodium)

Directions:

1. Heat olive oil in a large pot over medium heat. Add the ground turkey, season with a pinch of salt and pepper, and cook until browned, breaking it into small pieces as it cooks.
2. Add the diced carrots and celery to the pot, and sauté for a few minutes until they start to soften.
3. Pour in the low-sodium chicken broth and bring to a boil. Stir in the rice, reduce heat to a simmer, cover, and cook for about 20 minutes, or until the rice is tender and the vegetables are fully cooked.
4. Adjust seasoning with salt and pepper if needed. Serve hot.

Nutritional Information:

Per serving: 320 calories, 26g protein,
38g carbohydrates, 8g fat, 3g fiber,
60mg cholesterol, 180mg sodium,
450mg potassium, 220mg phosphorus.

13. Fish Chowder (Kidney-Friendly)

Yield: 4 servings | Prep Time: 15 minutes | Cook Time: 25 minutes

Ingredients:

- 1 pound white fish (e.g., cod, haddock), cut into bite-size pieces
- 2 cups diced potatoes, skin removed (choose low-potassium varieties)
- 4 cups low-sodium fish or vegetable broth
- 1 cup skim milk
- 1 onion, chopped
- 2 stalks celery, chopped
- 2 tablespoons olive oil
- Salt and pepper to taste (minimal salt for low sodium)
- Fresh parsley for garnish

Directions:

1. Heat olive oil in a large pot over medium heat. Add onion and celery, and sauté until softened, about 5 minutes.
2. Add the low-sodium broth and diced potatoes to the pot. Bring to a boil, then reduce heat and simmer until potatoes are just tender, about 10 minutes.
3. Add the fish pieces to the pot and simmer gently until the fish is cooked through, about 5-7 minutes.
4. Stir in the skim milk and heat through without boiling. Season with a pinch of salt and pepper to taste.
5. Serve hot, garnished with fresh parsley.

Nutritional Information:

Per serving: 250 calories, 27g protein, 20g carbohydrates, 5g fat, 2g fiber, 55mg cholesterol, 150mg sodium, 500mg potassium, 200mg phosphorus.

14. Pumpkin Soup (Low Sodium)

Yield: 4 servings | Prep Time: 10 minutes | Cook Time: 20 minutes

Ingredients:

- 4 cups pumpkin puree (fresh or canned without added salt)
- 4 cups low-sodium vegetable broth
- 1 medium onion, diced
- 2 cloves garlic, minced
- 1/2 cup cream
- 1 tablespoon olive oil
- Salt and pepper to taste (minimal salt for low sodium)
- Fresh parsley or thyme for garnish (optional)

Directions:

1. Heat olive oil in a large pot over medium heat. Add onion and garlic, sautéing until onion is translucent, about 5 minutes.
2. Stir in the pumpkin puree and low-sodium vegetable broth. Bring to a gentle boil, then reduce heat and simmer for 15 minutes, allowing flavors to meld.
3. Use an immersion blender to puree the soup directly in the pot until smooth. Alternatively, carefully transfer the soup to a blender in batches and blend until smooth.
4. Stir in the cream and heat through for another 5 minutes, without boiling. Season with a pinch of salt and pepper to taste.
5. Serve hot, garnished with fresh parsley or thyme if desired.

Nutritional Information:

Per serving: 200 calories, 3g protein, 25g carbohydrates, 10g fat, 6g fiber, 30mg cholesterol, 150mg sodium, 400mg potassium, 100mg phosphorus.

Dessert Oasis: 16 Irresistibly Sweet Treats

1. Vanilla Rice Pudding

Yield: 4 servings | Prep Time: 5 minutes | Cook Time: 25 minutes

Ingredients:

- 1 cup low-protein rice
- 4 cups skim milk
- 1 teaspoon vanilla extract
- 1/4 cup sugar substitute

Directions:

1. Rinse the rice under cold water until the water runs clear.
2. In a medium saucepan, combine the rinsed rice and skim milk. Bring to a boil over medium heat, then reduce the heat to low.
3. Simmer gently, stirring occasionally, until the rice is tender and the mixture has thickened, about 20-25 minutes.
4. Remove from heat and stir in the vanilla extract and sugar substitute until well combined.
5. Divide the pudding into serving dishes. Serve warm, or chill in the refrigerator for at least 2 hours if preferred cold.

Nutritional Information:

Per serving: 180 calories, 5g protein, 30g carbohydrates, 0.5g fat, 0g fiber, 2mg cholesterol, 100mg sodium, 200mg potassium, 150mg phosphorus.

2. Lemon Berry Sorbet

Yield: 4 servings | Prep Time: 15 minutes (plus freezing time) | Cook Time: 0 minutes

Ingredients:

- 2 cups mixed berries (strawberries and blueberries), fresh or frozen
- Juice of 2 lemons
- 1/3 cup sugar substitute

Directions:

1. If using frozen berries, let them thaw slightly. Place the berries, lemon juice, and sugar substitute in a blender or food processor. Blend until smooth.
2. Taste the mixture and adjust sweetness if necessary by adding a little more sugar substitute.
3. Pour the mixture into a shallow dish and freeze for 1-2 hours, until it starts to set around the edges.
4. Stir the mixture every 30 minutes to break up any large ice crystals, until it's completely frozen and has a smooth, sorbet-like texture.
5. Serve immediately or transfer the sorbet to an airtight container and freeze until ready to serve.

Nutritional Information:

Per serving: 70 calories, 1g protein, 17g carbohydrates, 0g fat, 3g fiber, 0mg cholesterol, 10mg sodium, 150mg potassium, 50mg phosphorus.

3. No-Bake Cheesecake Cups

Yield: 4 servings | Prep Time: 15 minutes | Cook Time: 0 minutes (Refrigerate for at least 2 hours)

Ingredients:

- 8 ounces low-fat cream cheese, softened
- 1/4 cup sugar substitute
- 2 tablespoons lemon juice
- 1/2 cup graham cracker crumbs (low-sodium)

Directions:

1. In a mixing bowl, beat the low-fat cream cheese, sugar substitute, and lemon juice until smooth and creamy.
2. In four small cups or dessert dishes, evenly distribute the graham cracker crumbs to form the base layer.
3. Spoon the cream cheese mixture over the graham cracker crumbs in each cup, smoothing the tops with the back of a spoon.
4. Refrigerate the cheesecake cups for at least 2 hours, or until set, before serving.
5. Optionally, garnish with a small amount of lemon zest or fresh berries for added flavor and presentation before serving.

Nutritional Information:

Per serving: 180 calories, 6g protein, 15g carbohydrates, 9g fat, 0g fiber, 30mg cholesterol, 200mg sodium, 150mg potassium, 100mg phosphorus,

4. Peach Compote with Whipped Cream

Yield: 4 servings | Prep Time: 10 minutes | Cook Time: 5 minutes

Ingredients:

- 4 cups peaches (canned in juice), drained
- 1/4 cup sugar substitute
- 1 teaspoon vanilla extract
- 1 cup low-fat whipped cream

Directions:

1. In a medium saucepan, combine the drained peaches, sugar substitute, and vanilla extract. Cook over medium heat for about 5 minutes, until the peaches are warm and the flavors have melded together.
2. Allow the peach compote to cool slightly. You can serve it warm or chill it in the refrigerator for about an hour if you prefer it cold.
3. Divide the peach compote among four serving dishes.
4. Top each serving with a dollop of low-fat whipped cream just before serving.

Nutritional Information:

Per serving: 120 calories, 2g protein, 25g carbohydrates, 2g fat, 2g fiber, 5mg cholesterol, 40mg sodium, 190mg potassium, 50mg phosphorus.

5. Chocolate Mousse

Yield: 4 servings | Prep Time: 15 minutes |
Cook Time: 0 minutes (Chill for at least 1 hour)

Ingredients:

- 2 ripe avocados, peeled and pitted
- 1/4 cup cocoa powder
- 1/4 cup sugar substitute
- 1/2 cup skim milk
- 1 teaspoon vanilla extract

Directions:

1. In a blender or food processor, combine the avocados, cocoa powder, sugar substitute, skim milk, and vanilla extract. Blend until the mixture is smooth and creamy.
2. Taste the mousse and adjust the sweetness if needed by adding a little more sugar substitute.
3. Divide the mousse into serving dishes and chill in the refrigerator for at least 1 hour to set.
4. Before serving, you can garnish with a sprinkle of cocoa powder or fresh berries for added flavor and presentation.

Nutritional Information:

Per serving: 200 calories, 4g protein, 18g carbohydrates, 14g fat, 7g fiber, 0mg cholesterol, 40mg sodium, 300mg potassium, 100mg phosphorus.

6. Almond Biscotti

Yield: 4 servings | Prep Time: 20 minutes |
Cook Time: 40 minutes

Ingredients:

- 2 cups flour
- 1/2 cup almonds, chopped
- 1/2 cup sugar substitute
- 2 egg whites
- 1 teaspoon vanilla extract

Directions:

1. Preheat oven to 350°F (175°C). Line a baking sheet with parchment paper.
2. In a mixing bowl, combine flour, chopped almonds, and sugar substitute.
3. In another bowl, beat the egg whites and vanilla extract until frothy. Fold into the dry ingredients until the dough comes together.
4. Form the dough into a log shape on the prepared baking sheet. Bake for 25 minutes.
5. Remove from oven, let cool for a few minutes, then slice diagonally into 1/2-inch thick slices. Lay the slices flat on the baking sheet.
6. Bake for an additional 15 minutes, turning halfway through, until dry and golden.
7. Cool on a wire rack before serving.

Nutritional Information:

Per serving: 200 calories, 6g protein, 35g carbohydrates, 5g fat, 2g fiber, 0mg cholesterol.

7. Pineapple Upside-Down Cake

Yield: 6 servings | Prep Time: 20 minutes | Cook Time: 35 minutes

Ingredients:

- 1 can (20 ounces) pineapple slices in juice, drained (reserve the juice)
- 1/4 cup sugar substitute
- 1 box low-sodium cake mix (yellow or white)
- Ingredients called for by cake mix (replace oil with applesauce if possible to reduce fat)
- Maraschino cherries without pits (optional, for garnish)

Directions:

1. Preheat your oven according to the cake mix package instructions. Prepare a 9x13 inch baking pan by lightly greasing it.
2. Arrange pineapple slices at the bottom of the prepared baking pan. If desired, place a maraschino cherry in the center of each pineapple slice.
3. Prepare the cake mix according to the package instructions, substituting oil with applesauce if recommended and using the reserved pineapple juice as part of the liquid component if possible. If more liquid is needed, add water to make up the difference.
4. Pour the cake batter over the pineapple slices in the baking pan.
5. Bake according to the cake mix package's instructions, or until a toothpick inserted into the center of the cake comes out clean.
6. Let the cake cool in the pan for about 10 minutes, then carefully invert it onto a serving plate.
7. Serve warm or at room temperature.

Nutritional Information:

Per serving: 220 calories, 3g protein, 50g carbohydrates, 3g fat, 1g fiber, 0mg cholesterol, 200mg sodium, 100mg potassium, 150mg phosphorus.

8. Berry Parfait

Yield: 4 servings | Prep Time: 10 minutes | Cook Time: 0 minutes

Ingredients:

- 2 cups low-fat Greek yogurt
- 2 cups mixed berries (such as strawberries, blueberries, raspberries)
- 1/4 cup sugar substitute
- 1 cup low-protein granola

Directions:

1. In a small bowl, mix the Greek yogurt with the sugar substitute until well combined.
2. In serving glasses or bowls, create layers starting with a spoonful of Greek yogurt, followed by a layer of mixed berries, and then a sprinkle of low-protein granola.
3. Repeat the layers until the ingredients are used up, finishing with a layer of berries on top.
4. Chill in the refrigerator for a few minutes before serving, or serve immediately if preferred.
5. Optionally, garnish with a mint leaf or a drizzle of honey (if not avoiding extra sugar) for added flavor and presentation.

Nutritional Information:

Per serving: 220 calories, 12g protein, 30g carbohydrates, 4g fat, 3g fiber, 10mg cholesterol, 80mg sodium, 300mg potassium, 150mg phosphorus.

9. Coconut Rice Balls

Yield: 4 servings | Prep Time: 20 minutes |
Cook Time: 30 minutes (plus chilling time)

Ingredients:

- 1 cup cooked low-protein rice
- 1/2 cup coconut milk
- 1/4 cup sugar substitute
- 1/2 cup shredded coconut, unsweetened

Directions:

1. In a medium saucepan, mix the cooked rice with coconut milk and sugar substitute. Cook over medium heat, stirring frequently, until the mixture is thick and creamy, about 15-20 minutes.
2. Allow the rice mixture to cool to a manageable temperature. Then, wet your hands slightly to prevent sticking and form the rice mixture into small, bite-sized balls.
3. Roll each rice ball in shredded coconut until well coated.
4. Place the coconut-covered rice balls on a plate and chill in the refrigerator for at least 1 hour to set.
5. Serve chilled as a delightful, kidney-friendly dessert or snack.

Nutritional Information:

Per serving: 150 calories, 2g protein, 20g carbohydrates, 7g fat, 1g fiber, 0mg cholesterol, 30mg sodium, 100mg potassium, 80mg phosphorus.

10. Carrot Cake Muffins

Yield: 6 servings | Prep Time: 15 minutes |
Cook Time: 20 minutes

Ingredients:

- 2 cups flour
- 1 1/2 cups grated carrots
- 1/2 cup sugar substitute
- 2 teaspoons low-sodium baking powder
- 2 teaspoons cinnamon
- 1/2 cup unsweetened applesauce
- 1/2 cup skim milk
- 2 egg whites

Directions:

1. Preheat your oven to 350°F (175°C). Line a muffin tin with paper liners or lightly grease with cooking spray.
2. In a large bowl, whisk together the flour, sugar substitute, low-sodium baking powder, and cinnamon.
3. Stir in the grated carrots.
4. In another bowl, mix the applesauce, skim milk, and egg whites until well combined.
5. Add the wet ingredients to the dry ingredients, stirring just until moistened. Avoid overmixing.
6. Spoon the batter into the prepared muffin tin, filling each cup about three-quarters full.
7. Bake for 20 minutes, or until a toothpick inserted into the center of a muffin comes out clean.
8. Let the muffins cool in the pan for 5 minutes, then transfer to a wire rack to cool completely.

Nutritional Information:

Per serving: 180 calories, 5g protein, 35g carbohydrates, 1g fat, 3g fiber, 0mg cholesterol, 80mg sodium, 200mg potassium, 100mg phosphorus.

11. Apple Cinnamon Crisp

Yield: 4 servings | Prep Time: 15 minutes | Cook Time: 30 minutes

Ingredients:

- 4 medium apples, peeled, cored, and sliced
- 1 teaspoon cinnamon
- 1/4 cup sugar substitute
- 1 cup low-sodium granola

Directions:

1. Preheat your oven to 375°F (190°C). In a mixing bowl, toss the sliced apples with cinnamon and sugar substitute until evenly coated.
2. Spread the apple mixture in an even layer in a baking dish.
3. Sprinkle the low-sodium granola evenly over the apples.
4. Bake in the preheated oven for about 30 minutes, or until the apples are tender and the topping is lightly browned.
5. Let cool for a few minutes before serving. Can be enjoyed warm or at room temperature.

Nutritional Information:

Per serving: 200 calories, 2g protein, 45g carbohydrates, 2g fat, 5g fiber, 0mg cholesterol, 50mg sodium, 250mg potassium, 100mg phosphorus.

12. Pumpkin Spice Pudding

Yield: 4 servings | Prep Time: 10 minutes | Cook Time: 15 minutes

Ingredients:

- 2 cups pumpkin puree
- 2 cups skim milk
- 2 teaspoons pumpkin spice
- 1/4 cup sugar substitute

Directions:

1. In a medium saucepan, whisk together the pumpkin puree, skim milk, pumpkin spice, and sugar substitute.
2. Cook over medium heat, stirring constantly, until the mixture begins to bubble slightly. Reduce the heat to low and continue to stir for about 10-15 minutes, or until the pudding has thickened.
3. Remove from heat and let the pudding cool for a few minutes. Then, pour into serving dishes.
4. Chill in the refrigerator until set, about 2 hours.
5. Serve chilled, optionally garnished with a sprinkle of pumpkin spice or a dollop of whipped cream.

Nutritional Information:

Per serving: 120 calories, 6g protein, 20g carbohydrates, 0.5g fat, 3g fiber, 2mg cholesterol, 60mg sodium, 240mg potassium, 100mg phosphorus.

13. Poached Pears in Cinnamon Syrup

Yield: 4 servings | Prep Time: 10 minutes | Cook Time: 20 minutes

Ingredients:

- 4 medium pears, peeled, halved, and cored
- 2 cinnamon sticks
- 1/4 cup sugar substitute
- 4 cups water

Directions:

1. In a large saucepan, combine the water, sugar substitute, and cinnamon sticks. Bring to a simmer over medium heat, stirring until the sugar substitute is fully dissolved.
2. Carefully add the pear halves to the simmering liquid. Reduce the heat to maintain a gentle simmer and cover.
3. Poach the pears for 15-20 minutes or until they are tender when pierced with a knife but still hold their shape.
4. Carefully remove the pear halves from the liquid and set aside to cool slightly. Continue to simmer the liquid uncovered, until it has reduced by half and thickened into a syrup.
5. Serve the pears warm or chilled, drizzled with the cinnamon syrup.

Nutritional Information:

Per serving: 100 calories, 1g protein, 25g carbohydrates, 0g fat, 5g fiber, 0mg cholesterol, 10mg sodium, 200mg potassium, 50mg phosphorus.

14. Angel Food Cake

Yield: 8 servings | Prep Time: 20 minutes | Cook Time: 45 minutes

Ingredients:

- 12 egg whites, at room temperature
- 1 cup flour
- 1 1/2 cups sugar substitute (ensure it's suitable for baking)
- 1 1/2 teaspoons cream of tartar
- 1 teaspoon vanilla extract
- A pinch of salt

Directions:

1. Preheat your oven to 350°F (175°C). Have a 10-inch tube pan ready (do not grease the pan).
2. In a large bowl, beat the egg whites with the cream of tartar and a pinch of salt until soft peaks form.
3. Gradually add the sugar substitute while continuing to beat until stiff peaks form. Beat in the vanilla extract.
4. Sift the flour over the egg white mixture in three additions, gently folding in after each addition until just blended. Be careful not to deflate the egg whites.
5. Pour the batter into the ungreased tube pan and smooth the top with a spatula.
6. Bake for 45 minutes, or until the cake is golden brown and springs back when lightly touched.
7. Invert the pan onto a bottle or cooling rack immediately after baking and let cool completely upside down (this helps the cake maintain its volume).
8. Once cool, run a knife around the edges of the pan, including the central tube, to release the cake. Serve as is or with a dollop of whipped cream and fresh berries.

Nutritional Information:

Per serving: 120 calories, 4g protein, 15g carbohydrates, 0g fat, 0g fiber, 0mg cholesterol, 100mg sodium, 90mg potassium, 50mg phosphorus.

15. Strawberry Gelatin Cups

Yield: 4 servings | Prep Time: 10 minutes |
Cook Time: 0 minutes (plus refrigeration time)

Ingredients:

- 1 package sugar-free strawberry gelatin (0.3 to 0.6 ounces, depending on brand)
- 2 cups boiling water
- 1 cup fresh strawberries, sliced

Directions:

1. In a mixing bowl, dissolve the sugar-free strawberry gelatin in 2 cups of boiling water. Stir until completely dissolved.
2. Allow the gelatin mixture to cool to room temperature. Once cooled, gently stir in the sliced strawberries.
3. Pour the gelatin and strawberry mixture into individual serving cups or a large mold if preferred.
4. Refrigerate for at least 4 hours, or until the gelatin is fully set.
5. Serve chilled, optionally garnished with additional fresh strawberry slices or a dollop of whipped cream.

Nutritional Information:

Per serving: 10 calories, 2g protein,
0g carbohydrates, 0g fat, 1g fiber,
0mg cholesterol, 30mg sodium,
50mg potassium, 20mg phosphorus.

16. Custard with Berry Sauce

Yield: 4 servings | Prep Time: 15 minutes |
Cook Time: 10 minutes (plus chilling time)

Ingredients:

- 4 egg yolks
- 2 cups skim milk
- 1/4 cup sugar substitute
- 1 teaspoon vanilla extract
- 1 cup mixed berry sauce (prepared from fresh or frozen berries with a sugar substitute)

Directions:

1. In a medium saucepan, whisk together egg yolks, sugar substitute, and skim milk. Cook over medium heat, stirring constantly, until the mixture thickens enough to coat the back of a spoon, about 10 minutes. Do not allow it to boil.
2. Remove from heat and stir in the vanilla extract.
3. Pour the custard through a fine-mesh sieve into a bowl to remove any lumps. Divide the custard evenly among four serving dishes.
4. Chill the custard in the refrigerator until set, about 2 hours.
5. Before serving, top each custard with an even layer of the mixed berry sauce.
6. Serve chilled.

Nutritional Information:

Per serving: 150 calories, 8g protein,
20g carbohydrates, 4g fat, 1g fiber,
185mg cholesterol, 125mg sodium,
250mg potassium, 200mg phosphorus.

Chapter 5: 30-Day Meal Plan.

A step-by-step guide to a month of kidney-friendly eating.

Mapping Out Your Renal Diet Journey

Week 1

Day	Breakfast	Lunch	Snack	Dinner	Dessert
1. *Monday*	Classic Egg White Scramble	Quinoa Tabbouleh Twist	Crispy Garlic Toasts	Herb-Grilled Chicken with Quinoa Salad	Vanilla Rice Pudding
2. *Tuesday*	Low-Sodium Blueberry Muffins	Lean & Green Turkey Avocado Wrap	Zesty Lemon Hummus	Lemon-Dill Salmon	Lemon Berry Sorbet
3. *Wednesday*	Sunrise Soothe Kidney-Friendly Pancakes	Kidney Care Caprese Salad	Cucumber Dill Bites	Vegetable Stir-Fry with Tofu	No-Bake Cheesecake Cups
4. *Thursday*	Morning Bliss Almond Milk Berry Smoothie	Hearty Veggie Stew	Herbed Greek Yogurt Dip	Garlic Butter Shrimp	Peach Compote with Whipped Cream
5. *Friday*	Dawn Delight Apple Cinnamon Oatmeal	Refreshing Egg White Salad Sandwich	Savory Baked Apple Chips	Roasted Turkey Breast with Thyme	Chocolate Mousse
6. *Saturday*	Fresh Start Avocado Toast on Low-Sodium Bread	Simplified Dill Salmon Patties	Mini Rice Cakes with Avocado and Tomato Salsa	Creamy Low-Potassium Mushroom Risotto	Almond Biscotti
7. *Sunday*	Cozy Cinnamon Rice Pudding	Zesty Zucchini Noodles with Lemon-Herb Dressing	Cheesy Cauliflower Popcorn	Balsamic Glazed Beef	Pineapple Upside-Down Cake

Week 2

Day	Breakfast	Lunch	Snack	Dinner	Dessert
8. *Monday*	Blissful Berry Yogurt Parfait	Herb-Infused Roasted Cauliflower Steaks	Mini Rice Cakes with Avocado and Tomato Salsa	Lemon-Dill Salmon Bake	Peach Compote with Whipped Cream
9. *Tuesday*	Garden Fresh Zucchini Bread	Balsamic Glazed Chicken Breast	Cucumber Dill Bites	Creamy Cauliflower Soup	Chocolate Mousse
10. *Wednesday*	Morning Greens Kale and Mushroom Sauté	Quinoa Tabbouleh Twist	Cheesy Cauliflower Popcorn	Vegetable Curry with Coconut Milk	Almond Biscotti
11. *Thursday*	Cozy Cinnamon Raisin Bread Pudding	Zesty Zucchini Noodles with Lemon-Herb Dressing	Herbed Greek Yogurt Dip	Pork Tenderloin with Apple Compote	Vanilla Rice Pudding
12. *Friday*	Energizing Cranberry Walnut Toast	Bright Mediterranean Chickpea Salad	Savory Baked Apple Chips	Garlic Herb Shrimp Skewers	Lemon Berry Sorbet
13. *Saturday*	Honeyed Greek Yogurt with Almonds	Whole Wheat Broccoli and Cheese Pasta	Kale Chips with Sea Salt	Eggplant Parmesan Light	No-Bake Cheesecake Cups
14. *Sunday*	Morning Harvest Veggie Egg Muffins	Lean & Green Turkey Avocado Wrap	Vegetable Spring Rolls	Herb-Grilled Chicken with Quinoa Salad	Berry Parfait

Week 3

Day	Breakfast	Lunch	Snack	Dinner	Dessert
15. *Monday*	Cozy Cinnamon Rice Pudding	Refreshing Egg White Salad Sandwich	Herbed Greek Yogurt Dip with Vegetable Sticks	Grilled Portobello Mushrooms with Herb Quinoa Salad	Coconut Rice Balls
16. *Tuesday*	Lean Green Cheesy Spinach Omelet	Zesty Lemon Pepper Tilapia with a Side of Kale and Apple Salad	Savory Baked Apple Chips	Vegetable Stir-Fry with Tofu	Carrot Cake Muffins
17. *Wednesday*	Morning Bliss Almond Milk Berry Smoothie	Kidney-Friendly Stuffed Bell Peppers	Mini Rice Cakes with Avocado and Tomato Salsa	Creamy Low-Potassium Mushroom Risotto	Pumpkin Spice Pudding
18. *Thursday*	Fresh Start Avocado Toast on Low-Sodium Bread	Crisp Cucumber Cream Cheese Sandwiches	Zesty Lemon Hummus with Cucumber Slices	Lemon-Dill Salmon with Roasted Asparagus Spears	Poached Pears in Cinnamon Syrup
19. *Friday*	Sunrise Protein-Packed Egg White and Turkey Sausage Burrito	Hearty Savory Lentil Soup with a Side of Quinoa Salad with Veggies	Cucumber Dill Bites	Baked Cod with Paprika and a Side of Sesame Green Beans	Angel Food Cake with Fresh Berries
20. *Saturday*	Golden Sunrise Tofu Scramble	Crispy Chickpea Salad	Oven-Roasted Chickpeas	Maple-Glazed Pork Chops with Sweet Potato Wedges	Chocolate-dipped Fruit
21. *Sunday*	Morning Glow Peachy Keen Smoothie	Avocado Chicken Wrap	Cheesy Cauliflower Popcorn	Stuffed Turkey Meatloaf with Steamed Broccoli	Lemon Berry Sorbet

Week 4

Day	Breakfast	Lunch	Snack	Dinner	Dessert
22. Monday	Sunrise Quinoa Berry Bowl	Hearty Veggie Stew	Sesame Green Beans	Garlic Butter Shrimp with a side of Herb-Infused Roasted Cauliflower	Strawberry Gelatin Cups
23. Tuesday	Morning Greens Kale and Mushroom Sauté	Crisp Kale and Apple Salad with Walnuts	Cucumber Dill Bites	Roasted Turkey Breast with Thyme and a side of Beetroot and Goat Cheese Salad	Poached Pears in Cinnamon Syrup
24. Wednesday	Cozy Cinnamon Raisin Bread Pudding	Simplified Dill Salmon Patties with a side of Refreshing Berry Watermelon Slush	Savory Baked Apple Chips	Zucchini Lasagna	Custard with Berry Sauce
25. Thursday	Dawn Delight Apple Cinnamon Oatmeal	Whole Wheat Broccoli and Cheese Pasta	Mini Rice Cakes with Avocado and Tomato Salsa	Vegetable Curry with Coconut Milk	Apple Cinnamon Crisp
26. Friday	Blissful Berry Yogurt Parfait	Balsamic Glazed Chicken Breast with a side of Quinoa Salad with Veggies	Herbed Greek Yogurt Dip with Vegetable Sticks	Spinach and Goat Cheese Stuffed Chicken	Chocolate Mousse
27. Saturday	Energizing Cranberry Walnut Toast	Zesty Zucchini Noodles with Lemon-Herb Dressing	Carrot and Zucchini Fritters	Eggplant Parmesan Light	Vanilla Rice Pudding
28. Sunday	Classic Egg White Scramble	Tuna Salad Scoop in Lettuce Cups	Vegetable Spring Rolls	Cod with Parsley Pesto and a side of Chilled Cucumber Soup	Peach Compote with Whipped Cream

Week 5

Day	Breakfast	Lunch	Snack	Dinner	Dessert
29. *Monday*	Golden Sunrise Tofu Scramble	Refreshing Egg White Salad Sandwich	Zesty Lemon Hummus with Cucumber Slices	Lemon-Dill Salmon with a side of Roasted Vegetable Ratatouille	No-Bake Cheesecake Cups
30. *Tuesday*	Morning Bliss Almond Milk Berry Smoothie	Crisp Cucumber Cream Cheese Sandwiches	Savory Baked Apple Chips	Vegetable Stir-Fry with Tofu	Lemon Berry Sorbet
30+. *Wednesday*	Sunrise Protein-Packed Egg White and Turkey Sausage Burrito	Bright Mediterranean Chickpea Salad	Mini Rice Cakes with Avocado and Tomato Salsa	Garlic Butter Shrimp with a side of Sesame Green Beans	Chocolate-dipped Fruit
30+. *Thursday*	Morning Harvest Veggie Egg Muffins	Lean & Green Turkey Avocado Wrap	Herbed Greek Yogurt Dip with Vegetable Sticks	Herb-Grilled Chicken with Quinoa Salad	Vanilla Rice Pudding
30+. *Friday*	Sunrise Quinoa Berry Bowl	Kidney Care Caprese Salad	Crispy Garlic Toasts	Eggplant Parmesan Light	Peach Compote with Whipped Cream
30+. *Saturday*	Fresh Start Avocado Toast on Low-Sodium Bread	Hearty Veggie Stew	Vegetable Spring Rolls	Creamy Low-Potassium Mushroom Risotto	Berry Parfait
30+. *Sunday*	Sweet Morning Banana Pancakes	Quinoa Tabbouleh Twist	Kale Chips with Sea Salt	Savory Beef Stew	Apple Cinnamon Crisp

Chapter 6: Strategies for Success: Incorporating Strategies to Maintain Motivation and Adherence to the Renal Diet

Embarking on the renal diet journey marks a significant step for individuals confronting kidney health challenges. It represents a holistic lifestyle adjustment designed to enhance kidney function and overall well-being. Central to this transition is cultivating a positive mindset and harnessing the power of education. This chapter explores these fundamental strategies, offering a guide to enduring motivation and commitment to the renal diet.

Developing a Positive Mindset

Achieving success in kidney health management through dietary means begins with fostering a positive mindset. This mindset transcends mere optimism; it acts as a dynamic force shaping behavior, decisions, and health outcomes. Key aspects include:

- **Acceptance:** Recognizing the necessity of a renal diet as a proactive health measure marks the first step toward acceptance. This perspective sees dietary adjustments as opportunities for enhancement rather than limitations.

- **Resilience:** The journey will inevitably present challenges. Building resilience enables individuals to face these obstacles with fortitude, maintaining focus on overarching health objectives.

- **Optimism:** An optimistic outlook drives motivation and promotes adherence to the renal diet. It's rooted in the belief in the transformative potential of dietary changes on kidney health and life quality.

Embrace the Power of Education

Comprehending kidney function and the dietary impact on kidney health is essential. Education empowers individuals to make enlightened health decisions, converting the renal diet from a mere set of rules into a valuable instrument for kidney disease management.

- **Equipping with Knowledge:** A deep understanding of kidney disease, its progression, and the influence of lifestyle elements like diet and physical activity on kidney health is vital. This broad perspective helps individuals grasp the significance of the renal diet in their health regimen.

- **Leveraging Resources:** A wealth of resources awaits those keen to expand their knowledge of the renal diet and kidney health. These resources include trusted online sources, educational materials from healthcare providers, support groups, and specialized workshops. Active engagement with these materials reinforces a sense of empowerment and dedication.

The path to kidney health via the renal diet is both a beacon of hope and a navigational tool through the complexities of chronic kidney disease. Yet, the journey extends beyond mere comprehension of the diet's nuances. The essence of success lies in the practical application of this knowledge, achieved by setting attainable goals and fostering a supportive atmosphere.

Setting Realistic Goals

Achievable Dietary Goals

The quest for optimal kidney health unfolds through gradual progression. Establishing realistic, achievable dietary goals is crucial. This process involves formulating specific, measurable, attainable, relevant, and time-bound (SMART) objectives, such as moderating sodium intake or integrating a certain number of kidney-friendly meals weekly. Tailoring these goals to personal health requirements and lifestyle ensures they are both stimulating and feasible.

Importance of Short-Term Milestones

Short-term milestones act as vital checkpoints en route to long-term aspirations. They offer immediate targets that, upon realization, enhance motivation and forward momentum. Acknowledging and celebrating these achievements, irrespective of their scale, significantly uplifts morale. For instance, adhering to the renal diet over a week merits recognition. Such accomplishments invigorate the journey, deterring disenchantment and fatigue.

By navigating the renal diet with informed strategies, individuals can maintain their course toward kidney health and overall well-being, transforming challenges into victories and restrictions into opportunities for growth and improvement.

Creating a Supportive Environment

Building a Support System

The complexity of navigating the renal diet greatly benefits from a supportive network, encompassing family, friends, healthcare professionals, and peers also managing kidney disease. Emotional support and practical assistance from loved ones, coupled with expert guidance from healthcare providers, including dietitians specializing in renal nutrition, are invaluable. Engaging with support groups or online forums offers a platform for sharing experiences and insights, fostering a strong sense of community.

Optimizing Your Living Space

An environment conducive to the renal diet is essential. Organizing the kitchen and pantry to prioritize kidney-friendly foods simplifies adherence to dietary guidelines. Labeling areas for foods low in sodium, potassium, and phosphorus aids in meal preparation, while keeping renal diet-friendly recipes readily available supports meal planning and reduces the temptation to stray from the diet. A well-arranged living space not only facilitates dietary compliance but also diminishes stress and enhances overall well-being.

The Joy of Learning and Experimentation

Continuous learning and culinary experimentation keep the renal diet engaging and sustainable. Exploring new flavors and cooking techniques can transform dietary restrictions into an exciting culinary adventure, encouraging creativity in the kitchen and making meals an opportunity for discovery. This approach not only enriches the dining experience but also bolsters diet adherence by preventing monotony.

Overcoming Obstacles

Despite best efforts, deviations from the diet may occur. It's crucial to view these lapses as learning opportunities rather than failures, focusing on immediate correction and future prevention. Recognizing and analyzing slip-ups, avoiding guilt, and planning for future success are key strategies for maintaining long-term diet adherence.

Conclusion

The journey to adhering to the renal diet is multifaceted, requiring more than just an understanding of dietary restrictions; it necessitates a comprehensive approach to lifestyle change. By implementing the strategies outlined in this chapter, individuals can confidently navigate the renal diet, transforming challenges into opportunities for success. The objective is to empower adherence to the diet, making it not only a medical necessity but also a rewarding lifestyle choice, thus enhancing kidney health and overall quality of life.

Bonus Chapter: 7 Festive Holiday Recipes Celebratory dishes that keep your kidneys in mind.

1. Herb-Roasted Turkey Breast

Yield: 4 servings | Prep Time: 20 minutes | Cook Time: 1 hour

Ingredients:

- 2 pounds boneless turkey breast
- 2 tablespoons olive oil
- 1 tablespoon fresh rosemary, chopped
- 1 tablespoon fresh thyme, chopped
- 3 garlic cloves, minced
- Salt and pepper to taste (minimal salt for low sodium)

Directions:

1. Preheat the oven to 375°F (190°C). Rinse the turkey breast and pat dry with paper towels.
2. In a small bowl, mix together the olive oil, rosemary, thyme, and garlic. Season lightly with salt and pepper.
3. Rub the herb mixture all over the turkey breast, making sure to coat it evenly.
4. Place the turkey breast in a roasting pan and roast in the preheated oven for about 1 hour, or until a thermometer inserted into the thickest part of the breast reads 165°F (74°C).
5. Let the turkey rest for 10 minutes before slicing. Serve warm.

Nutritional Information: 220 calories, 35g protein, 0g carbohydrates, 5g fat, 0g fiber, 85mg sodium, 300mg potassium, 200mg phosphorus.

The Herb-Roasted Turkey Breast is a celebration on a plate, perfectly suited for festive occasions while being mindful of health, especially for those on a renal diet. This elegant dish marries the succulence of boneless turkey breast with a fragrant rub of fresh rosemary, thyme, and garlic, delivering a burst of flavor in every bite. It caters to dietary needs without compromising on taste or quality.

2. Low-Sodium Green Bean Casserole

Yield: 4 servings | Prep Time: 15 minutes | Cook Time: 30 minutes

Ingredients:

- 1 pound fresh green beans, trimmed and cut into bite-sized pieces
- 8 ounces mushrooms, sliced
- 1 can (10.5 ounces) low-sodium cream of mushroom soup
- 1 cup crispy onions

Directions:

1. Preheat the oven to 350°F (175°C). Bring a large pot of water to a boil. Add the green beans and cook for 5 minutes until bright green and slightly tender. Drain and set aside.
2. In a skillet over medium heat, sauté the mushrooms in a splash of water or vegetable broth until they are soft and their liquid has evaporated, about 5-7 minutes.
3. In a large mixing bowl, combine the cooked green beans, sautéed mushrooms, and low-sodium cream of mushroom soup. Stir until the vegetables are well coated.
4. Transfer the mixture to a baking dish. Bake in the preheated oven for 20 minutes.
5. Sprinkle the crispy onions over the top of the casserole and bake for an additional 10 minutes, or until the top is golden and crispy.
6. Serve warm.

Nutritional Information: 150 calories, 4g protein, 20g carbohydrates, 7g fat, 4g fiber, 5mg cholesterol, 150mg sodium, 250mg potassium, 100mg phosphorus.

With fresh green beans at its heart, this casserole maintains the crisp, vibrant essence of the vegetable, enhanced by the earthy depth of sautéed mushrooms. The use of low-sodium cream of mushroom soup ensures that the dish remains creamy and indulgent, while keeping sodium levels in check. Topped with a golden layer of crispy onions, it delivers a delightful crunch that contrasts beautifully with the tender vegetables beneath.

Perfect for gatherings or a cozy family dinner, this Low-Sodium Green Bean Casserole proves that dietary restrictions don't have to mean compromising on taste or tradition. It's a testament to the joy of shared meals, offering a healthier option that's as satisfying as it is nutritious.

3. Roasted Butternut Squash Soup

Yield: 4 servings | Prep Time: 20 minutes | Cook Time: 40 minutes

Ingredients:

- 1 large butternut squash (about 2 pounds), peeled, seeded, and cubed
- 4 cups low-sodium vegetable broth
- 1/4 teaspoon nutmeg
- 1/4 teaspoon cinnamon
- 1 cup unsweetened almond milk
- Salt and pepper to taste (minimal salt for low sodium)

Directions:

1. Preheat the oven to 400°F (200°C). Spread the butternut squash cubes on a baking sheet, and roast for 25-30 minutes, or until tender and lightly caramelized.
2. In a large pot, combine the roasted butternut squash, low-sodium vegetable broth, nutmeg, and cinnamon. Bring to a simmer over medium heat.
3. Using an immersion blender (or in batches in a regular blender), puree the soup until smooth.
4. Stir in the almond milk, and continue to heat the soup until it's warm throughout. Season with salt and pepper to taste.
5. Serve warm, garnished with a sprinkle of nutmeg or cinnamon if desired.

Nutritional Information: 120 calories, 2g protein, 25g carbohydrates, 2g fat, 5g fiber, 55mg sodium, 400mg potassium, 50mg phosphorus.

The Roasted Butternut Squash Soup offers a velvety, heartwarming experience, perfect for chilly evenings or as a festive starter. This soup is a harmonious blend of the natural sweetness of butternut squash with the delicate spices of nutmeg and cinnamon, creating a dish that is both comforting and sophisticated. By roasting the squash first, it unlocks a depth of flavor and caramelization that elevates the soup beyond the ordinary.

Serving this Roasted Butternut Squash Soup can turn any meal into an occasion, offering a nourishing blend of flavors that cater to health without compromising on taste. It's a testament to how thoughtful ingredients and preparation can result in a dish that's both beneficial and beautifully indulgent.

4. Maple-Glazed Butternut Squash

Yield: 4 servings | Prep Time: 15 minutes | Cook Time: 30 minutes

Ingredients:

- 1 large butternut squash (about 2 pounds), peeled, seeded, and cubed
- 3 tablespoons maple syrup
- 1/2 teaspoon cinnamon
- 1/4 teaspoon nutmeg

Directions:

1. Preheat the oven to 400°F (200°C). In a large bowl, toss the cubed butternut squash with maple syrup, cinnamon, and nutmeg until evenly coated.
2. Spread the coated squash in a single layer on a baking sheet lined with parchment paper.
3. Roast in the preheated oven for 30 minutes, or until the squash is tender and the edges are caramelized, stirring halfway through the cooking time.
4. Remove from the oven and let cool slightly before serving.

Nutritional Information: 120 calories, 2g protein, 30g carbohydrates, 0.5g fat, 5g fiber, 0mg cholesterol, 10mg sodium, 480mg potassium, 55mg phosphorus.

Featuring cubes of butternut squash lovingly tossed in pure maple syrup and sprinkled with cinnamon and nutmeg, this dish is then roasted to perfection. The result is a tender, caramelized delight that highlights the squash's inherent sweetness, complemented by the subtle spice of cinnamon and nutmeg. This combination not only enhances the flavor profile but also fills the kitchen with a comforting, aromatic scent.

With only 120 calories per serving and a good source of fiber, the Maple-Glazed Butternut Squash is both health-conscious and satisfying. It's a versatile dish that pairs beautifully with a variety of mains, from roasted meats to vegetarian options, making it a fantastic addition to any dinner table, festive gathering, or cozy night in.

This recipe is a testament to the idea that managing dietary restrictions doesn't have to mean compromising on taste or enjoyment. It's a celebration of natural flavors, brought together in a way that's both simple and incredibly satisfying, ensuring that each bite is as nourishing as it is delicious.

5. Pear and Walnut Salad

Yield: 4 servings | Prep Time: 10 minutes | Cook Time: 0 minutes

Ingredients:

- 4 cups mixed greens
- 2 ripe pears, cored and thinly sliced
- 1/2 cup walnuts, toasted and chopped
- 1/4 cup balsamic vinaigrette (low sodium)

Directions:

1. In a large salad bowl, combine the mixed greens and sliced pears.
2. Sprinkle the toasted walnuts over the top of the greens and pears.
3. Drizzle the balsamic vinaigrette over the salad, and gently toss to coat all the ingredients evenly.
4. Serve immediately, or chill in the refrigerator for a refreshing and crisp salad.

Nutritional Information: 150 calories, 4g protein, 18g carbohydrates, 8g fat, 3g fiber, 0mg cholesterol, 150mg sodium, 350mg potassium, 95mg phosphorus.

The Pear and Walnut Salad is a delightful fusion of textures and flavors, meticulously designed to cater to those on a renal diet while ensuring a burst of fresh, palate-pleasing tastes.

At its heart, this salad features crisp mixed greens and thinly sliced ripe pears, offering a sweet and refreshing crunch with every bite. The addition of toasted walnuts introduces a nutty depth and a satisfying crunch, complementing the soft sweetness of the pears. This combination not only brings a variety of textures to the dish but also ensures a blend of nutrients beneficial for overall health.

The salad is elegantly dressed with a low-sodium balsamic vinaigrette, adding a tangy and slightly sweet layer that enhances the natural flavors of the greens and fruit. This choice of dressing aligns with the nutritional needs of those managing their sodium intake, without compromising on taste.

Ideal for serving as a refreshing starter, a light lunch, or a side dish, this salad is versatile and easy to prepare, requiring no cooking and minimal prep time. It's a testament to the fact that healthful eating can be simple, delicious, and accessible, making it a perfect addition to any meal, whether for everyday dining or special occasions.

6. Stuffed Mushrooms with Spinach and Feta

Yield: 4 servings | Prep Time: 20 minutes | Cook Time: 15 minutes

Ingredients:

- 16 large mushrooms, stems removed
- 2 cups spinach, chopped
- 1/2 cup feta cheese, crumbled
- 2 cloves garlic, minced
- 2 tablespoons olive oil

Directions:

1. Preheat the oven to 375°F (190°C). Arrange the mushroom caps on a baking sheet, cavity side up.
2. In a skillet, heat 1 tablespoon of olive oil over medium heat. Add the garlic and sauté until fragrant, about 1 minute.
3. Add the spinach to the skillet and cook until wilted, about 2-3 minutes. Remove from heat and let cool slightly.
4. In a bowl, combine the sautéed spinach and garlic mixture with the crumbled feta cheese.
5. Stuff each mushroom cap with the spinach and feta mixture. Drizzle the remaining olive oil over the stuffed mushrooms.
6. Bake in the preheated oven for 15 minutes, or until the mushrooms are tender and the tops are slightly golden.
7. Serve warm as a delicious and nutritious appetizer or side dish.

Nutritional Information: 100 calories, 6g protein, 4g carbohydrates, 7g fat, 1g fiber, 15mg cholesterol, 200mg sodium, 300mg potassium, 100mg phosphorus.

Crafted with large, succulent mushrooms as the base, this recipe transforms the simple ingredients of spinach, feta cheese, garlic, and olive oil into a sophisticated and flavorful appetizer or side dish. The mushrooms, known for their meaty texture and ability to absorb flavors, are filled with a mixture of sautéed spinach and garlic, offering a nutrient-rich filling that is both vibrant and aromatic. The addition of crumbled feta cheese introduces a creamy, salty dimension that complements the earthiness of the mushrooms and the freshness of the spinach.

Ideal for serving as an elegant appetizer or a light side dish, these stuffed mushrooms are sure to be a hit among guests, regardless of their dietary needs. They embody the principle that healthful eating can be both satisfying and full of flavor, making them a standout choice for any occasion where good food and good health are prized.

7. Festive Fruit Salad

Yield: 4 servings | Prep Time: 20 minutes | Cook Time: 0 minutes

Ingredients:

- 1 cup pineapple, diced
- 1 cup mandarin oranges, drained if canned
- 2 kiwis, peeled and sliced
- 1/2 cup pomegranate seeds
- 2 tablespoons fresh mint, chopped

Directions:

1. In a large mixing bowl, combine the diced pineapple, mandarin oranges, sliced kiwis, and pomegranate seeds.
2. Gently toss the fruits together until well mixed.
3. Sprinkle the chopped fresh mint over the fruit salad and gently mix again to distribute the mint throughout the salad.
4. Chill the fruit salad in the refrigerator for at least 10 minutes before serving to allow the flavors to meld together.
5. Serve the fruit salad chilled, garnished with additional mint leaves if desired.

Nutritional Information: 90 calories, 1g protein, 22g carbohydrates, 0g fat, 3g fiber, 5mg sodium, 250mg potassium, 30mg phosphorus.

The Festive Fruit Salad is a vibrant, refreshing dish that celebrates the natural sweetness and varied textures of fruits, complemented by the bright aroma of fresh mint. This dish is not only a feast for the eyes with its colorful array of pineapple, mandarin oranges, kiwis, and pomegranate seeds, but it also offers a delightful mix of flavors.

Nutritionally balanced, this fruit salad is low in calories yet rich in vitamins, antioxidants, and fiber, contributing to a healthy diet without compromising on taste. Its easy preparation and appealing presentation make it an ideal choice for festive occasions, family gatherings, or as a refreshing side dish to complement any meal.

Serving this Festive Fruit Salad not only brings a touch of elegance to the table but also provides a healthful option that can be enjoyed by everyone, especially those mindful of their kidney health. It's a testament to how simple ingredients, when thoughtfully combined, can create a dish that's both delightful and supportive of one's dietary needs.

As we reach the final page of "Super Easy Renal Diet Cookbook for Beginners 2024," I hope that the journey through these pages has been as enriching for you as it has been fulfilling for me to create. This cookbook was born out of a passion for helping individuals navigate the challenges of kidney health through delicious, nutritious, and easy-to-prepare meals. The path to managing kidney health can often seem daunting, but it is my deepest hope that this collection has illuminated the way with joy, flavor, and simplicity.

Remember, each recipe you've encountered here is more than just a set of instructions; it's a stepping stone towards a healthier, more vibrant life. The choices you make in the kitchen have the power to transform your health in profound ways. As you continue on your journey, let these recipes be your guide and companion, reminding you that a renal-friendly diet can be both satisfying and full of variety.

I encourage you to keep experimenting with the recipes, adapting them to your tastes and nutritional needs. Your diet is a powerful tool in your kidney health arsenal, and with each meal, you are taking a step towards better health.

Should you ever find yourself in need of inspiration or facing challenges, remember that you are not alone. The community of individuals managing kidney health is vast and supportive. Reach out, share your experiences, and continue to learn — for the journey to health is always evolving.

Thank you for allowing this cookbook to be a part of your renal diet journey. May the meals you prepare from these pages bring you not only health but also happiness and a sense of achievement. Here's to delicious meals that nourish both body and soul.

Wishing you health, happiness, and culinary delight,

Baily Lambert

P.S. Keep an eye out for future editions and updates as we continue to explore and expand the world of renal-friendly cooking. Your journey is ongoing, and so is our commitment to supporting you every step of the way.

Made in the USA
Las Vegas, NV
06 May 2024